John Ankenbruck

The Voice
of
The Turtle

The News Publishing Co.
Fort Wayne, Indiana 46802

To dear La Verne who loves the wilderness

Introduction

Anyone who grew up near the rivers and lakes of the Midwest feels a certain closeness with the Indians who went before along the same paths and waterways. It was a common thing to find an old arrowhead -- a direct link with the war parties of the Indian nations which once swept everything before them across the entire Great Lakes area.

There were the Ottawas, the Hurons, the Miamis, the Illinois, the Shawnees, the Delawares, the Potawatomis and the Kickapoos -- tribal names which have faded into legends. It was these Indian nations which joined in the most powerful Indian alliance in American history. For a generation they held their own against the main armies of the United States. Their leader was the Miami warchief, Little Turtle.

It is about this strange and clever Indian that John Ankenbruck writes. It is a tremendous story. I particularly like the broad historical perspective. For a period, the Turtle was virtual master of an area extending from Canada to the Ohio River and from Pennsylvania to the Mississippi. He was not the kind of hero Indian we have come to associate with names like Crazy Horse, Tecumseh or Cochese. Instead, he could be devious and even cruel -- and as callous as the American generals and politicians he faced. He was the master of strategy on the field of war. He was unrelenting in wiping out settlers and pioneers who tried to move west. He was tricky enough to play off the English against the Americans in the fight to control the Old Northwest.

In short, this is the story of a man, who was an Indian leader like none other. Though old records show he was the most significant Indian adversary and figure in the eyes of Presidents Washington and Jefferson, he has peculiarly faded from public memory. He was the only Indian chieftain able to hold back for many years the westward expansion of the U. S.

I think most readers will be fascinated with the story of the duel of this Indian warchief for the great wilderness against a whole series of invading armies of civilization.

CHRIS SCHENKEL
Lake Tippecanoe
January 1, 1974

Chapter 1

Damp and cold was the wind which blew across the squat buildings of the temporary Capitol of the United States. It matched the mood of the French attache as he approached the slush and mud of the Philadelphia street.

Twice the previous week he had waited half a morning in the outer chambers of the Executive Mansion, only to be told President Washington had concluded receptions for the day. It was February 1, 1797, and the minor French diplomat knew there was little real purpose in gaining a meeting with the American President in the final weeks of the Washington Administration.

The President had become increasingly testy, impatient and preoccupied. It was rumored that his health was uneven, possibly failing. Each day the attacks on him personally, and on his actions, assumed more bitter and destructive tones. The hero had grown goat horns. He was, in those final months, a generally unpopular and hated man.

But all this was somewhat beside the point for a young man seeking opportunity and protection of his position. The French government of the revolutionary Directoire was becoming less sure by the day. A record showing a consultation with the President Washington (still the hero of the age in Europe) was the sort of thing only the foolish would let slip away.

Citizen Jean Homfroi Hasard did not consider himself foolish. He rather enjoyed what he considered a provincial Philadelphia, partly because he felt superior to it. This made it easier for him to push beyond the usual protocol -- in fact, beyond considerate behavior. It didn't consciously occur to Hasard that he would hardly dare to press so rudely for a meeting with the head of state in Paris.

At that moment, though, his resolve was a bit watered. The main chance, which seemed so simple only days ago, was less firm. And, as he picked his way across the ruts

1

and wet snow, his footing also became uncertain. To avoid an unrushing carriage, he went to his left ankle in the native American slime.

Hasard found the waiting chamber of the Executive Mansion different from prior occasions only in that it was warmer and more crowded. The clerk was just as indifferent to his presence as before.

"Let me beg your pardon Monsieur Hasard, but as long as you are here today, perhaps you would like meeting a rather interesting chap who speaks your own language."

He followed the clerk across to a hall of white walls and unpolished wooden floors. They entered a large room, made bright by very high windows along the opposite wall. Hasard did hear French conversation, but of a guttural and sing-song quality which was quite strange to the continental ear.

The man speaking was sitting on a high stool with his right leg propped up on a pillow, the fashion for the gout-afflicted. His dress was odd. He wore woven breeches with a waist coat of animal skin, perhaps deer, which was open to the belt. He had silk stockings, but on his feet were slippers stitched with leather thongs. There was a cynical and cruel quality about the mouth which reminded Hasard of a Di Vinci drawing he had once seen.

The three men in the room turned to the Frenchman and nodded, but none arose for the introductions. A Mr. Stuart, in plain colonial garb, held a large drawing pad on his lap. A Monsieur Volney, who sat cross-legged in rather foppish-fashioned clothes, stared in a pout at what he obviously considered an intruder in the discussion.

The man on the stool was introduced as Mr. Chief Turtle. There was the suggestion of the dullness of dissipation in his smile. The Frenchman momentarily thought the man to be Arab or Spanish. The straight black hair was pulled back from a high forehead and hung past his collar. Around his neck was a silver strand and on his fingers were rings with large stones. Combined in the appearance was an obvious athletic quality verging toward age and self-indulgence. Hasard, the diplomat, guessed him to be under 50 and an American Indian, though this was the first

2

of the aborigines he had seen in gentle surroundings.

Constantin Volney, affecting an intellectual attitude and a lawyer's plausibility, resumed the conversation.

"Recent scientific thought has your people originally migrating across the Northern wastes from Asia." Volney articulated his French as if he were making a speech to himself, though he was talking to the Indian.

"We have it on the best authority that the entire savage nations are descended from the Tartars of the Far East. And, I must say, my own studies of language might very well bear this out."

The Indian, who was watching the snow fall past the high windows, continued to watch the snow.

"Have you lived among the Tartars?" he asked.

"That is hardly necessary," the language arts philosopher said.

"Have you lived among the Indians?"

"Of course not. You know yourself, however, that I have visited at length at posts in your western lands."

"Then tell me if you can. Why could not these Tartars have come from America? Or why could not the fathers of both peoples have been born in their own countries?"

Volney tilted his head to either side, as if to include Hasard and Stuart in some general mirth. He had begun an explanation about "academic skills" when the Indian cut him off by turning a question to the attache.

"Are you a Tartar?"

"I've been called worse," Hasard replied. "How does it feel to be a savage?"

The Indian laughed and became animated for the first time in the conversation. "We all might be beasts under the skin. And who can say that is not the better part?"

There will invariably be those persons who see it as their duty to impress newcomers with the importance of the company already there, including themselves. Volney faced Hasard and began speaking in expansive tones.

"This is the famous Indian Chief Little Turtle who led whole armies of savages against the military on the frontier. Mr. Stuart here is doing his portrait. President Washington has honored him on three occasions -- even

3

gave him a sword he carried in the War for Independence. The hero Kosciusco gave him the pair of pistols there on the table."

"I have heard the main army of the United States was practically annihilated twice in the Indian country a few years ago..." Hasard began to say.

"The very thing I am telling you about. I have it on the best of authority that the slaughter of the troops was greater than in any single battle of the Revolution. There have been efforts to conceal the losses. Several Senators charged the President was irrational and was far exceeding his authority in sending regulars into the territory. It was brutal -- on both sides. The Indians did some indescribable things ... so some people say."

"Why then," the diplomat asked, "is Washington honoring the very leader of the Indians who destroyed his troops?"

"Because after General Wayne's army later defeated the Indians, there was a peace treaty. The President, of course, wants to keep ... huh ... everyone happy."

Hasard asked the Indian if he were actually a prisoner, or whether he could return to his home.

"I can return when I wish Monsieur, but the Soldiers are always with me. They build me a large house and give me much land. But, you tell me, am I free?"

The attache decided to act the diplomat and changed the subject. "A relative of mine, a cousin of my mother, came over here years ago during the war. He was an officer of the French volunteers. According to records, he led a company of men into the Northwest wilderness.

"We never heard from him again. I was wondering, is there any chance you might have seen him? His name was August Mottin de la Balme."

The Indian chief lifted his gouty foot off the pillow and turned slowly toward the Frenchman. A half smile played about his parted lips. But the quickness of his eyes going to Hasard's hands, then back to his face, startled the Frenchman.

"Ah, that was many moons ago. You may tell your family the Chief of the Miamis saw their kinsman on his last day and that he was laid in a warm place."

4

Chapter 2

Little Turtle stood alone on the hillside. He was as motionless as the black walnut tree next to him. Only the eyelids moved. He squinted as he looked west to Aboite Creek which glistened slightly a quarter mile away in the cool evening sun.

The date was Nov. 3, 1780. At the distant creek there was some activity. A company of Americans, including more than 100 frontier riflemen, was busy making camp. The Indian chieftain reflected on the carelessness of the group as he watched sparks ignite several campfires. His gaze was attracted to a tall man in an ornate and unfamiliar uniform who appeared to be giving directions.

August Mottin de la Balme was unaware that he was the object of attention of some 500 braves of the Miami Indians and several allied tribes. He was deep in the wilderness of the Old Northwest -- in what is now Indiana a few miles from present Fort Wayne.

La Balme was in a rather elated mood. It had been a busy day, and one of the first profitable ones in some time for La Balme. He and his men, having completed a march up the Wabash River, had scattered a few Indians at Miamitown and raided the store houses of the French traders. They put the torch to the buildings and retired west with all the booty that horses and men could carry.

Up to this time, La Balme had been a man with big ideas, but no notable successes. He had been commissioned in France as a cavalry officer and came to America with the Marquis de Lafayette. He entered the service of the Thirteen States.

Soon, however, he appeared without apparent previous arrangement at Kaskaskia, an American outpost on the Mississippi. He immediately began to round up forces for a campaign through the domain of the hostile Miamis to attempt capture of the English bastion at Detroit. As far as is known, this was not a sanctioned American military expedition. Rather, the enterprise was of a more private nature. La Balme may have entered into a scheme even before he left France, with the aim of joining with French Canadians to appropriate lands and wealth along the contested American-Canadian frontier.

It was a time of contradictions. As Little Turtle waited in the forest, he neither knew nor cared that Benedict Arnold had a few days earlier deserted to the British after trying to subvert the American fort at West Point; or that at King's Mountain in the Carolinas, the colonials had just gained a minor victory over the invading English. Those events were a thousand miles away.

In the peculiar political world of the Northwest, the French traders found their better interests were on the side of the English and the Indians. The principal victims of La Balme's attack at Miamitown had been, in fact, the French tradesmen who had large trading interests there.

Though Little Turtle was French educated and spoke French rather than English, he was unimpressed by the alliance of France with the United States in the Revolutionary War. The Miamis were at war with the colonials who attempted to move into their lands. This made the Indians allies of the English. And in contrast with some other Indian leaders who sought talks and agreements, Little Turtle had decided the best defense was extermination of all intruders.

When La Balme first arrived at American outposts on the Mississippi, he received immediate encouragement. Any strike against the hated Indians was automatically cheered by American frontiersmen. But a pat on the back was quite another thing from going into the Indian country. La Balme failed to conscript men in the numbers he had hoped. After many weeks at Kaskaskia and some more time at Vincennes on the lower Wabash, he started up river with something less than 100 men. He still hoped to be joined by 400 more frontier types at Post Ouiatenon, near the present city of Lafayette.

This failed to materialize. La Balme recruited several dozen volunteers, but lost a number of wary associates who had a change of mind about proceeding any further.

The immediate aim of the expedition was to take

6

Miamitown on the Maumee River where the St. Joseph and St. Mary Rivers converge. It was a semi-civilized, thriving community that was also called Kekionga by the Indians. It was a hub of trading activity in the Old Northwest due to its being the only portage point in a series of waterways from the Great Lakes to the Gulf of Mexico. It was the chief town of the Miami Indian nation, which controlled an area which today includes the city of Chicago, southern Michigan, and much of Ohio, Indiana and Illinois, down to the Ohio River. Villages of the Delawares and Shawnees, both allies of the Miamis, were also in the vicinity. The Miamis were viciously anti-American and few pioneers ever ventured far into their territory.

But La Balme, the French cavalry officer, struck at Miamitown - a move that George Rogers Clark had ruled out on his expedition on the lower Wabash the previous year.

Taking the post at the three rivers turned out to be surprisingly easy for the La Balme forces. After setting fire to the buildings, they retired to a previously-planned encampment along Aboite Creek. There they looked over the materials, provisions, furs and valuables taken in the raid.

As the day faded, the La Balme party broke out bottles of rum from the filched stores and sat in small groups around the fires. Anecdotes about the lack of resistance in the raid vied with stories of past campaigns. Laughter could be heard far into the night.

Little Turtle did not find the hours of the evening difficult to bear. He was by nature a patient and meticulous person. As he directed the cautious surrounding of La Balme's camp, he wore only deerskin coverings on his legs and was naked above the waist, as was the Miami habit in war, even in cold weather. His face was carefully painted and ear rings were affixed to his ears.

This was the night that Little Turtle was to enter into the history books. And before his life would run its course, he was to twice lead the strongest Indian armies ever assembled and employed in battle on the North American continent. He would be accused of cruelty and

7

deviousness. His habits of thought were very unlike those usually associated with Indians. But as long as he was to retain political control of the allied Indian tribes, he would be successful.

As he stood near the dark Aboite, the Turtle was 28 years old and exhibited the easy confidence of a young man whose experiences had so far been without setbacks. Two braves approached. The young chieftain raised the palm of his hand and made a swinging motion. The braves then returned into the chill darkness. Otherwise, he hardly moved or spoke until after midnight.

The Indians raked the sleeping forces of La Balme with rifle shot. They then jumped them with knives, axes and stone-embedded clubs. The lucky were killed instantly. The attack was vicious and short -- so short there was time for but brief chaos.

Forty of the Americans were killed by rifle shot or beaten to death. The others, about 70 men in varying stages of health, were taken prisoner. Little Turtle directed that the scalps be removed from the dead. He would be paid later for them by the British commander at Detroit.

The Indians lost but five of their party. These bodies were removed and carried several miles to the Miami burial grounds located on a hillside by the St. Mary's River. The bodies of the white men were left to rot at the site. This may have given the stream a name which has lasted to this day. With the coming of warm weather the following spring, French traders passing along a portage some distance away called the place "Abattoir" for slaughter house, so-called because of the odor which pervaded the area for some months. Another tradition has it that the name Aboite came from a different corruption of the French. This was the term "aux abois" or instant of death.

Little Turtle and his aging relative, Le Gris, were working under torch light late into the night, as they fingered through the baggage of French adventurer, La Balme. The Turtle tossed firearms and other items of value to various braves. There was one thing, however,

8

which particularly interested him. This was a long list of French names. Included in the list was the identity of practically every French trader who was then a resident of the Miamitown area. Little Turtle later gave the list to the British commander of the Detroit garrison. It is still in existence today at the Detroit Public Library, and remains the most complete and accurate record of the French families who lived at the post by the three rivers during the Revolutionary War period. Since France and the United States were allies, perhaps this was considered a list of traitors. At that time, the Frenchmen in the wilderness sided with the Indians and English, thereby risking death penalties.

The Indians along the Aboite began pushing and dragging the prisoners toward the main village of Kekionga at Miamitown. Little Turtle waved to Le Gris that he was ready to go. There were no women with the La Balme company, so he saw little reason to linger at the scene. The sun was already up by the time the two chiefs reached their village.

It was late in the afternoon when Little Turtle, now rested, walked into the clearing area at Miamitown. Few braves were to be seen, but commotion, shouts, smoke and screams quickened his senses.

Old women and children were excitedly running back and forth between fires and a number of tree trunks to one side of the compound. At the fires, long sticks were being held in the flames. Here and there ends of old rifle barrels were similarly held. These items were then rushed to the tree trunk area.

The survivors of the previous night's battle had had a long day. Leather thongs had been strapped about each man's arms, which were pulled overhead, binding them to the trunks of the trees. Four or five men were tied in this upright position to each tree.

Some of the prisoners, those wounded more seriously the night before, were now dead. Others also were hanging slack from the ropes, too exhausted for more than momentary reaction when scorched by the sticks and iron butts being jabbed at them. Most, however, were

9

thrusting about with great animation, protecting themselves the best they could in the limited area of movement.

Little Turtle walked by indifferent to the whole procedure. He had seen it all many times before. The tall cadaverous Le Gris, a cousin of the Turtle, pointed in the direction of La Balme and his aide-de-camp, Monsieur Rhy. Both of the captives were tied to a tree in a similar fashion to the others. La Balme was on his seat with his back to the tree trunk. He could not answer the Turtle. Part of his chin had been shot away in the battle along the swampy creek, some 10 miles to the west. His eyes had a wide-open stunned expression. It was clear that he was near death.

After a brief talk with Rhy, Little Turtle ordered the young aide-de-camp to be removed from the tree and taken to a windowless hut. Rhy was later delivered to the English military at Fort Ponchartrain at Detroit for questioning. He eventually made his way to Fort Niagara where he described the end of La Balme and his men.

The end was two days in coming. In addition to amusing themselves with the surviving captives, the Indians seemed to be waiting for something. That something arrived on the second morning. It was the White Skin family -- a rather well-known but hardly hallowed clan in that era.

Usually when early American or English-speaking authorities mention the rituals of White Skin, the words "revulsion" or "indescribable" or "depravity" are employed. General Lewis Cass, governor of the Michigan Territory, and Father Stephen Theodore Badin, a missionary instrumental in the founding of the University of Notre Dame, both clearly substantiated the activities of the White Skin society among the Miami Indians.

It remained, however, for several French traders to leave in the records full and frank accounts of what was going on. One of these fur traders, Jean Battiste Bruno, gives eyewitness descriptions. His and other stories indicate the White Skin clan had cannibal appetites.

Regarding the clan, one branch lived at Eel River, some 35 miles northwest of Miamitown and the other branch lived along Calumet Lake, now within the city limits of

Chicago. When they weren't eating people, the clan tanned. They tanned the skins of wild animals for Indian and French traders, such as Bruno. The Eel River location, some miles west of Little Turtle's village at a place called Devil's Lake is today farm lands and clover fields. The Calumet site, approximately at Stony Island and 115th St., has fared less well with the ages. The air is still foul with unpleasantness, the lands of the disorderly district of south Chicago being given over to industrial waste and carbon monoxide.

The soldiers of the La Balme group were hardly thinking that far ahead. Taking one's own life was commonly held in that era to be preferable to capture by the Indians. The prisoners, however, had neither the means nor choice to do anything but await the end. They were taken on the second day to a rise of ground on the east bank of the St. Joseph River, about a mile north of the junction with the Maumee. The remains of an old French fort, once taken by the English and then captured by the Indians during the Pontiac uprising in 1763, was still standing a short distance away.

In the meantime, Little Turtle departed on a hunting trip. He wasn't particularly interested in what was going to take place, though he valued the practice as a means of instilling fear in the enemies of the Miamis. He left Le Gris to look after things.

Hundreds of Indians from miles around had assembled at Miamitown for the event. It was about noontime when the White Skin clan arrived from a village along the Eel River. The other Indians, particularly those new to the area, stared at them with obvious curiosity. The faces of the entire clan were painted black -- including the squaws and children. They shuffled along quietly toward the torture grounds just to the north on the river shore.

After a bit, Indians of various tribes again took up the howling chants. Shouts mingled with gusts of wind on that warm and dry November afternoon. As the surviving captives of the La Balme company were dragged along the river bank, their exhaustion contributed to a dream-like quality. Stakes were already firmly projecting up from

11

the earth when they came to the cleared place. The captives looked sheepishly around. Several of the men had the smiles of the embarrassed, as if it were awkward to be the center of all this attention.

Dry leaves, kindling and small logs were built around the feet of the prisoners, who were strapped naked to the stakes. This was mainly squaw's work. The braves passed the time in games, dances and speeches. The White Skin clan sat impassively and watched as the fires were ignited. They did not participate in the killing. Yells, however, went up from both the other Indians and the damned.

Flames and smoke swirled around the men at the stakes. Most were dead within an hour. The White Skin group was huddled near one of the victims, watching with careful interest. Jean Battiste Bruno, the fur trader, reported in detail.

"When dead, the body was laid upon burning coals until well cooked. After a prolonged ceremony, the father of the clan cut off a piece for each member of the family, presenting it to them on a sharpened stick while they sat in a circle around the fire. After the family received portions, he asked in a loud voice if any others wanted to participate in the eating. Several men and squaws came forward awkwardly and seated themselves in the circle. Deep silence prevailed until the end of the ritual." Bruno also told of other instances of cannibalistic rites at Calumet Lake in Chicago and on the lower Wabash River.

Chief Richardville, who became head of the Miamis in a later era, said the Miamis had early formed a man-eating society as a weapon of terror to their enemies -- first other tribes and later American pioneers. The practice was largely confined to the one family and its descendants. French missionaries for nearly 100 years attempted to end the savage practice, and reportedly were successful in many instances. However, it was not until the end of the 18th Century that the rites became extinct.

Acts of inhumanity became increasingly common on the frontier as the Indians and the colonists joined in a life-death struggle for the lands of the Old Northwest. There are in existence literally thousands of reports of killings,

12

torture and scalping by both white men and Indians. There is a further aspect which cannot be ignored because of the numerous substantiated reports. It is quite clear that large numbers of Indians enjoyed the spectacle of torture and suffering. It seems to have been a part of their culture. Whole families would get together for these events. It was like a big game in which children, women and men had their special parts to play.

Chapter 3

The waters of the Maumee were swirling with the spring thaw as the British political agent Alexander McKee and two Shawnee Indians pulled their canoe onto the mud bank of Miamitown.

Little Turtle and old Chief Pacan watched quietly from a heavy timber house as Le Gris went to meet the visitors. It was a damp chilly day of 1783 and a rather sober occasion. The Turtle already knew the reason for McKee's appearance.

With the coming of peace at the end of the Revolutionary War, the British embarked on a mission of duplicity that was to cost both the Americans and the Indians. Formally, England and the United States were on normal terms, with the English ceding the lands of the Old Northwest to the States. Actually, they had no intention of relinquishing their hold on trade and politics in the hinterland. To the Indians, the treaty was worse than nothing. It was their lands which were being traded by the political powers.

Entering the house with McKee were the Shawnee Chief, The Snake, and his cousin, Captain Johnny. The three Miami chiefs and their guests sat down to a meal of venison, wild turkey, raccoon and rum. A rather smoky fire crackled along the side wall where soot clung thickly to the black surface.

"Colonel Arent Schuyler de Peyster sends his greetings to the great chiefs of the Miamis," McKee said as they began their discussions. The agent looked directly at Pacan. He said the British were fearful that continued Indian raids across the Ohio River on the settlements of Kentucky, Virginia and Pennsylvania would bring a stronger American military reaction to the Northwest.

"But the white men are already on our side of the river," Pacan said, ignoring that the British had already ceded both sides of the river -- a fact McKee also didn't mention under the immediate circumstances.

14

"Then take their scalps on this side," McKee said. "Believe me, the English will never desert their Indian friends. You have Colonel de Peyster's word on it, and mine also."

"What are the Shawnee going to do," Pacan asked, looking from McKee to The Snake.

McKee, however, answered. "They, and the Delawares too, have agreed with His Majesty's Government that the tribes will benefit when the raids across the Ohio are stopped. All the Indian people will be better off if there is restraint at this time." The Snake nodded his head, then looked furtively to the side at Little Turtle.

For many weeks, the forest pipelines had kept the Turtle informed about the visits of McKee to the various tribal villages north of the Ohio River. The agent had been sent by de Peyster, the British commander at Detroit, to convince the Indians of a new policy. The British, who planned to continue their military presence at Detroit, Fort Niagara, Mackinac, St. Joseph near Lake Michigan and other posts on American territory, wanted a low profile.

"How will the Miami benefit," the Turtle asked.

"We promise better prices for furs and special gifts to all the chiefs. Also, Colonel de Peyster will help bring all the tribes together. This will be very important to you in resisting further moves by the Americans."

"We need more guns," the Turtle said. "We need 200 more rifles and gun powder now. We will need more later."

"Will the Miami agree to remain on the north side of the Ohio," McKee asked.

"If you will .." Pacan began to say, but the Turtle cut in.

"We make no promises. Our head chief Pacan here and I will go to Detroit. We will see our friend Colonel De Peyster and what he might have for us. Then maybe we can decide."

McKee then passed out large jugs of rum to each of the Indians. Le Gris and the two Shawnees immediately uncorked theirs and proceeded to pour down the liquid. Little Turtle, Pacan and McKee walked out into the open. The Turtle previously knew most of the other tribes had

15

agreed to draw back from the attacks across the Ohio. He also knew The Snake would never stick to the bargain, and would be taking revenge on the Kentuckians for the raids of George Rogers Clark on the Shawnee villages. Besides, the American pioneers were floating in larger numbers down the Ohio.

The quarters of Colonel Arent Schuyler de Peyster at Detroit were luxurious by any standards, but particularly so for a post so far from the usual civilized climes.

Little Turtle knew, however, the plush rooms were mainly inherited by the British from the comfort-loving French commandants who had occupied Fort Detroit in an earlier generation. The Indian was impressed just the same with the gracious hospitality of his host. With the Turtle were Chief Pacan and Le Gris. They and about 100 Miami warriors had descended the Maumee and crossed Lake Erie to the Detroit River. As was his usual practice in negotiations, Little Turtle let Pacan, the hereditary head of the Miamis, carry the burden of the conversation.

De Peyster was telling the Miami representatives of British hopes for the bringing together of the Indians into a massive confederation. The British commander, small, trim and immaculately dressed in a gilded and red uniform, fancied himself to be a poet. He was speaking in drawing room tones and exposing ruffled white cuffs as he waved his hand grandly in emphasis.

Little Turtle was not deceived by the gentle manner. He knew that de Peyster, of all the British commanders, was the most chillingly quick and remorseless. Formerly the commandant at Fort Mackinac, de Peyster had assumed the Detroit post after the blundering Henry Hamilton had been captured by the Americans at Vincennes. He paid better for scalps and instinctively sorted out useful information from the phony rumors constantly current in the wilderness. He maintained a network of spies from the American Capitol at Philadelphia to posts and villages west of the Mississippi River.

"I would like now to introduce Sir John Johnson, who has been speaking with the leaders of the Six Iroquois

Nations," de Peyster said. "It is hoped the Miami Nation and the other western tribes will meet this fall to affect a grand Indian alliance."

Sir John looked at Pacan, Little Turtle and the cadaverous Le Gris as if he had a bad taste in his mouth; though in fact he had just sipped a glass of claret. "The great Mohawk Chief Joseph Brant," Sir John said, "has consented to take the lead in forming a confederation of both the eastern and western tribes that will truly hold back the Americans from the ancestorial lands of the Indians. A council of 35 nations is to meet on the Sandusky River in the Huron country." All of Sir John's remarks were relayed by a translator to the French-speaking Miamis.

At the mention of Brant and the Iroquois, Little Turtle and Le Gris exchanged glances. De Peyster, who had been watching for the Indians' reaction, noted the cool eye movement of the otherwise impassive Miami chieftains. If the Americans were the recent and bitter enemies, the Iroquois were the ancient and hated enemies that every Miami knew from childhood. Generations before, the Miamis had migrated down from the Hudson Bay area to the western shores of Lake Michigan. They had then moved eastward along the rivers and lakes as far as Lake Erie and the Ohio River. Until this time the Iroquois had been dominant in those places.

The Miamis, together with the Illinois Indians, the Ottawas, the Chippewas, the Potawatomis and the Mingo, had fought a hundred year's war with the Six Nations of the Iroquois that decimated the populations on both sides -- reducing the number of Indians in the entire Great Lakes area to about one-third of what it had been. In the years since, remnants of many other Indian tribes, fleeing both the Iroquois and the colonials, had settled in the relatively protected area of the Miamis. These tribes included the Delaware and Shawnee in large numbers and a few Mohicans.

"We will discuss the meeting with our people and give you an answer," Little Turtle said. He then rose and left the room. In addition to his distrust of the Iroquois, the Turtle could not stomach the verbose and self-seeking

17

Brant. He had made up his mind that the Miami would not join the Iroquois, and surmised that de Peyster suspected as much. It was more politic for both, however, to let Sir John play out his role as visiting diplomatist.

There was one further thing. Little Turtle, war chieftain of all the Miamis, was a Mohican on his mother's side -- one of the few of that race not exterminated by the Iroquois.

It was much later that night when Little Turtle and Colonel de Peyster sat down for a private exchange. They eyed each other carefully, though both affected a relaxed mood. Not mentioned during the talks earlier in the day, in the presence of the visiting Foreign Ministry official and Indian chiefs, was a matter of particular concern to the Turtle. But first the amenities.

De Peyster held in his right hand something which glittered in the candle light of the otherwise dim room at the Detroit post. It was a heavy gold watch with engraved scrollwork on the cover. He handed it across to the Miami.

"Gen. Haldimand asked me to present this personally to you," De Peyster said, "as an indication of our esteem for our friends. I hope the good governor's faith is not misdirected," he added with a quick wink.

"Please tell him he will get his money's worth. The Miami will be even more grateful if we can have those other things we will be needing very soon now," Little Turtle said, pocketing the watch.

"Fulfilling your request for more rifles could be quite awkward if they were to fall into the wrong hands. As we have already explained, Gen. Haldimand has been given express advice from the Crown that attacks to the south of the Ohio are to be restrained. I would hope that none of the new rifles would ever be found there by the Americans."

"Ah, colonel, assure the good governor that the Miamis will only use the guns for hunting in the forest, nothing more. Yes, just hunting in the forest," Little Turtle said. "We can give our old rifles to the Shawnee. Who then can blame either of us if The Snake should again start his raiding parties on the Ohio?"

18

"I will see to it that you get the weapons, but say nothing about it until after you leave here," de Peyster said.

Later, de Peyster in his report to Frederick Haldimand, British governon-general of Canada, gave a slightly different story.

"The Indians are well disposed to refrain from further attacks against the Kentucky settlements. I doubt not, however, that I shall find some difficulty to restrain the Wabash Indians, but nothing shall be neglected that may in any way contribute to bring it about," the Detroit commander wrote.

While the English were telling the Indians that the Ohio River was the boundary between their possessions and those of the Americans, the United States Congress passed the Ordinance of 1783 which said just the opposite. The American declaration verbally wrested from the Indians all the lands between the Ohio River and Lake Erie, the Maumee River and the Great Miami River. The Congress reasoned the Indians, by supporting the British cause in the war, had forfeited all right to their lands. To the Indians, the American ordinance was a declaration of war. This was soon recognized, and a more moderate approach of gradual advance and subversion of the Indians was begun by the Americans. The first move was to divide the various Indian tribes. In this effort, the Indians were to cooperate only too well.

The Turtle was not quite the child of the wilderness that was so often seen as the typical condition of the Indian. He was a constant traveler over the French-speaking part of the New World, making trips to Montreal, Quebec and Louisiana, as well as the closer frontier posts. He understood the need of the western Indians for material support from the British in the growing battle with the Americans. Little Turtle also knew that the one who bestows gifts often gains more than the one who receives.

"I am leaving two Panis with you to serve in your household," the Turtle said to de Peyster, the one-time New York Tory who was now the most avid anti-American in the British military. By Pani, Little Turtle was using the French word for Pawnee, which to the Miami meant slave. The Miamis purchased slaves from the Pawnee Indians of the western plains. The slaves were possibly Sioux or other breed of plains Indians which the Miami considered inferior peoples. Later that day, the Miamis started on the trip back to Miamitown. The things they needed from de Peyster were eventually delivered.

Le Gris, tall and gaunt, had a speech impediment and one eye. He was a village chief among the Miamis but a major fear among the neighboring tribes. Except when he was with Little Turtle, Le Gris was almost always alone. Women would pull their children from his path. Young braves would mimic his shuffling walk, but never within his sight. No one knew how old he was, because even as a young man, he seemed already aged.

With Le Gris, the Turtle could be assured that information would always be wrung from any captive. The French traders used to tell the story of a particularly strong-willed prisoner who refused to talk after several specialists in this sort of thing tried every physical discomforture. The man held out for days.

Finally, Le Gris arrived back in Kekionga from Miami villages of Chicago on Lake Michigan's south shore and St. Joseph north of South Bend's present site. After two hours in a hut alone with Le Gris, the captive told everything he knew. "I never touch him," Le Gris said.

When Little Turtle heard that the British were planning to support a massive Indian confederation headed by the Mohawk Chief Joseph Brant, he quickly came to two conclusions. It was not that the Turtle was opposed to the idea of a confederation, but rather that it was a question of who would participate in such a confederation and who would be its leader. First, Little Turtle decided the Mohawks and other Iroquois nations to the east could not be trusted. Therefore the Miamis would seek to separate off the Iroquois tribes from any Indian alliance formed to fight the Americans. The second move involved Le Gris. The Turtle decided it would be to his own advantage if the Mohawk chief never arrived at the coming conference of the Indian tribes at a location along the south shores of Lake Erie.

He sent Le Gris on a quiet mission. A few days later, Le

Gris, with an ancient Buffalo hide wrapped about his shoulders in spite of the summer weather, was seen heading east toward the New York Indian villages. With him were seven Kickapoo warriors who were sometimes employed by the Miami chiefs for certain purposes. The poplar trees were shedding and the rivers and the earth of the forest were covered with the odd stringy things as the group went along its way.

It was about at this time that Chief Brant decided to take a trip to England, ostensibly to convince the British of the Indians' need for help at the diplomatic level in their disagreements with the Thirteen States. To be sure, the English and the Americans were in the midst of discussions of the disposal of Indian lands. No one could say whether the Iroquois chief was made aware of Le Gris and his movements in the territory, or if that had any bearing on his plans for an ocean voyage.

A year later, Chief Brant had his meeting, but many of the tribes did not attend. The Iroquois soon entered into negotiations with the state governments of Pennsylvania and New York, and a little later, a Congressional Commission. They were told "You are a subdued people. We shall declare to you the conditions on which you can be received into the peace and protection of the United States."

The Iroquois accepted the terms in which they gave up all the claims to their historic lands west of New York and Pennsylvania. A few years later, Chief Brant attempted to talk the other tribes into coming to terms with the Americans. He failed, largely due to Little Turtle and the Miamis, and their allies, the Shawnees. Brant, with the flavor of sour grapes, told the American representative: "Some tribes, rather than enter headlong into a destructive war, will give up a small part of their country. On the other hand, the Miamis, the Shawnees and the Kickapoos, who are addicted to horse stealing, as that kind of business is their best harvest, will of course declare for war, and not giving up any of their territory."

At about this time, the Iroquois, who from the beginning of the colonial period were the scourge of the New World, came to the end of the line. They never again figured in any significant way in the American historical struggle.

21

Chapter 4

The Shawnee raiding party came hurriedly into Miamitown with seven captives taken during battles with the Kentucky militia.

The Indians were nearly exhausted. Sitting on the ground in the humid August heat, they told of a large force headed by George Rogers Clark and Daniel Boone which was coming north, destroying villages and killing any Indians they could find along the way. Little Turtle soon sent scouts south to seek out the whereabouts of the American force. In the meantime, the Shawnees were holding more than forty scalps in the air, and were describing a series of battles south of the Ohio River.

It was a few weeks before, in the early 1780s, that a party of 400 Indians, mostly Shawnees, attacked the Kentucky post of Bryan's Station, about five miles north of Lexington. The Indians assaulted the fort twice, but were driven back by the fifty riflemen in the stockade. The Shawnees were stung with about 12 killed. They settled down in the cover of the woods and tried to draw out the pioneers in the fort.

The following day, Kentucky reinforcements consisting of some 45 men, mostly horsemen, made a dash for the fort. The Indians killed six of the group as they made the run for the stockade. One of the men killed was named Abraham Lincoln, who had recently come from Virginia along the wilderness paths. He left six children, one of whom was Tom; who became a wandering labor boy; eventually married a fatherless girl named Nancy Hanks, and had a little boy named after his grandfather.

The Snake, Chief Blackfish and Simon Girty, a white renegade, studied the Indian situation as they set siege to the fort. They were already aware that at least two runners from the fort had broken through the Indians and would be spreading the alarm to other Kentucky settlements.

The three raiding party leaders began to argue among themselves. Chief Blackfish said the Indians had missed their chance and should cut out. Girty, angry because of the fruitless attack, wanted to hit the fort again, using fire at night. The Snake said the Indians would stay under cover of the woods and await developments. This latter course is what they did.

The Indians got action soon enough. Strong forces from both Boonesborough and Harrodsburg were joined by the Kentucky militia from Lexington under Colonel John Todd. The force included 181 mounted riflemen. With a rush of hooves and shouting, they swept toward Bryans Station. They saw a chance to give severe and permanent punishment to the Indians, but they failed to reckon with The Snake, the military disciple of the Turtle.

The Indians pulled out and the Kentuckians went after them. The pursuit drew the militia about forty miles to the Licking River, not far south of its outflow into the Ohio River. The Snake concealed the Shawnees and others in the brush along a narrow ravine. They could see the Kentucky horsemen moving up the valley. They waited.

When the militia was within forty feet, the Indians fired their old British-made muzzle loaders, then went up from the ravine with hand weapons. Colonel Todd, reeling from his horse, was choked in the swampy waters. The Kentuckians fled south with the Indians clawing at them from the rear. They crossed the river, with the Indians swimming the stream in pursuit. The surviving Kentuckians never stopped until they reached Bryans Station the 40 miles away.

Once there, they were met by an even larger company of Americans -- more than 400 frontiersmen from more distant settlements. The surviving militia turned around, joined the reinforcements and started back toward the site of battle at the Licking River. When they got there, all was quiet. Sixty-one bodies, all scalped, were found. Seven more had been captured by the Shawnees. The Indians had departed for villages north of the Ohio.

General Clark formed a large expedition to punish the Indians. From the Louisville area they moved up river and crossed into the Indian country. North of the Ohio

23

along the Miami River, they almost caught up with the raiding party. The Indians fled, but the Kentuckians and Virginians who had joined them burned villages over a wide area. The whites took the scalps of five warriors they shot. They also killed a number of Indian women and children.

In this growing series of nightmares, even the larger American force soon took on the aspects of the prey. Miami, Kickapoo and Delaware parties slipped south in an effort to get below the plundering army of General Clark, as Little Turtle tried to draw it further up the Miami River. But as the Turtle soon learned from the runners, Clark suddenly returned across the Ohio after scattering the Shawnee villages. By that time, the seven captives taken at the Licking ravine were burned at the stake.

Families never recover from warfare -- a very personal thing. Back at the Licking River during the massacre of the Kentucky militia, Daniel Boone had lifted the body of his son off the Kentucky earth. The frontiersman had been fleeing across a field. He came across his son Israel, who had been cut down by a lead ball in the side of the head. The color had already drained from the boy's face. He was dead.

At that moment, a number of Shawnees appeared at the far side of the clearing. Boone had to leave the body of the boy and run with the others for the safety of Bryans Station. Two days later he returned with the reinforcements. He buried the mutilated remains.

Bitterness was becoming a daily diet for the pioneers to the south of the Ohio River. Boone wrote Governor Harrison of Virginia: "I have encouraged the people in this county all that I could; but I can no longer justify them or myself to risk our lives here under such extraordinary hazards. The inhabitants of this county are very much alarmed at the thought of the Indians bringing another campaign into our country again this fall. If this should be the case, it will break up these settlements. I hope, therefore, your excellency will take this matter into consideration, and send us some relief as quick as

24

possible.''

Just two years prior to his son's death, Boone had seen his brother, Squire, killed and scalped. Similar experiences were common to nearly every family in Kentucky and elsewhere in the Ohio River area. The pioneers had cut their way across the mountains and had labored for years to clear land and establish homesteads. In doing so, they had muscled out the few Indians who occasionally used the Kentucky area for hunting grounds. The wilderness area south of the Ohio, however, had been rather sparse in the way of resident Indians.

But with the coming of large numbers of settlers across the mountains and down the Ohio, the Indians became incensed. They saw the game disturbed and growing threats to their ancestorial lands. The attacks increased in frequency and scale. Women were attacked. Children were kidnapped.

Most of the Kentuckians suffered through it all. They stayed for another decade when a large part of the area was finally rendered safe. But with the coming of safety, one more disaster was to befall the pioneers.

When danger abated, shallow opportunists flowed west into the Kentucky counties. Shrewd land speculators worked with corrupt courts which were set up. The speculators hired surveyors to go into the settled country and chart more accurate property descriptions than had been made originally. Armed with these, they obtained legal title to the lands from the courts.

The result was predictible. The industrious pioneers, who had survived the loss of husbands, wives and children, and numerous privations, disease and attacks, lost their stakes and homes to the legally-oriented newcomer.

Daniel Boone did not move to the Missouri Territory in his declining years because he wanted ''elbow room'' as the old stories sometime tell it. Boone lost every foot of his land in Kentucky because of questions of legal title. His complaints to the state government were frustrated by well-placed state officials who were believed profiting in the land speculations. Many other pioneers had similar experiences. Land broke, they either went further west, back east, or looked towards the Indian lands north of the

Ohio River, which Congress was promising to the veterans of the Revolution.

In the harsh political chemistry of the frontier, there was one other type of man -- one who was already at home in the smoky village lands of the Indians, yet was like a watchful animal between two worlds. If there was a dirty word in those days, its name was Simon Girty.

Simon was a white renegade who lived among the Indians since he was kidnapped in childhood from a Pennsylvania farm. He was a large brutal man with savage changes in temperament and a penchant for drunken brawls.

When Little Turtle saw Girty arrive with a party of Shawnees under The Snake, he found he had a bad taste in his mouth. The Turtle did not trust white men in his war campaigns. But even among people of the villages on peaceful days, Simon was someone to be reckoned with.

The action came quickly enough. Little Turtle, Pacan and several other chiefs were having a parley that same night when they heard shouts and consternation coming from a hut down by the St. Mary's River. They soon found Simon Girty and his brother George working over an Indian in a cloud of dust. Simon was making ripping motions with a large blade as George attempted to hold the Shawnee by his deerskin clothing.

Simon and George Girty (George lived with a Delaware squaw at a place along the Maumee east of Miamitown, not far from the present Ohio-Indiana line) had been drinking rum for many hours with several Shawnee braves. Arguments and drunken wagers led to tests of strength. These soon developed into murderous swipes.

Simon Girty was born in 1744, the son of a pack-horse driver who was killed by an Indian. When Simon was 12 years old, he and his three brothers were grabbed by a Delaware raiding party. Also taken were the boys' mother, Mary, and her second husband, John Turner. The family watched as the Indians burned Turner to death. The mother disappeared and was never seen again.

Simon, George and James Girty were passed around the

26

Indian country and became a part of the wilderness society. James Girty later had a Shawnee squaw and traded regularly at Detroit, Miamitown and the Lake Erie area. Simon took for his wife a young girl named Catherine Malotte, who was kidnapped from a pioneer family that had been traveling to Kentucky in a flatboat down the Ohio River. The other brother, Thomas, returned to Pittsburgh in early life and remained loyal to the United States.

Loyalty was not one of Simon's stronger traits. After maturing with the Huron Indians, he returned to Fort Pitt for awhile as an interpreter. He ducked out, however, during the Revolution and joined in with many raids against the Americans during the following years. He led Shawnees in the burning out of homesteads and the hitting of settlements in western Pennsylvania and across the Ohio into Kentucky.

When Colonel William Crawford's American force met with disaster at the hands of Indian warriors near Sandusky, Girty laughed as Crawford was being burned to death at the stake. There were dozens of other unpleasantries reported over the years. The very mention of Girty was enough to bring curses to lips from New York to Kentucky and make people go for their guns. The unstable Girty, however, was on occasion capable of considerable bravery and kindness. He risked his own neck to save Simon Kenton, an American scout in the Old Northwest, who had been captured and marked for death by the Indians.

There were hundreds of men and women on the frontier who would have shot Girty on sight. Detachments of horsemen went after him. But Girty always managed to either elude or fight off his pursuers. He also managed to outlive most of them. In spite of a number of wounds and his joining in major skirmishes and battles in the wilderness over a 30-year period, Girty died of old age in Canada in the year of 1818. He was buried by several Huron Indians during a snow blizzard across the river from Detroit.

For a time, Girty had a landmark on the American scene. This was Girty Town in west-central Ohio. But one

27

of the first things the American settlers did when they moved into the area was rub out the old name and call the place St. Mary's.

With still another kidnapped child, a mother's love and tenacity was almost beyond measure. One day late in 1783, Little Turtle was watching along the south bank of the Maumee as a large group of Delaware Indian families came into Miamitown.

There was nothing unusual in this, because migrations of eastern Indians through the three rivers portage area had become an almost daily occurance. With the ending of the Revolutionary War, some of the tribes of New York, Pennsylvania and Virginia had been driven out by the state governments and had fled west.

What was unusual to Little Turtle, however, was the long auburn hair which hung nearly to the waist of a girl of a Delaware family. The Miami chief asked that the family be brought to him. He was told by the Indian couple that the girl, then 10 years old, had been with them for five years -- originally at their village near Niagara Falls. The Indian family had fled the Americans, going across Ontario north of Lake Erie, to a temporary village near Detroit. The next leg of the trip had been by the water route down to the present site of Fort Wayne.

This little girl was Frances Slocum. Schools and public institutions in Fort Wayne and towns in the Wabash Valley today bear her name. At Little Turtle's suggestion, the family, together with the little girl, settled at a Delaware village just east of three rivers.

Some years later, the girl with the auburn hair married a Delaware brave. Their Indian home was destroyed when the troops of General Josiah Harmar attacked Miamitown in 1790 and she was still living in the same vicinity during the campaigns of General Arthur St. Clair in 1791 and Anthony Wayne in 1794. She remarried, this time to a Miami chief, and the couple fled Miamitown when the Americans swept in with scorched earth tactics in October, 1794. They moved to a place along the Mississinewa River near present day Peru.

The full story of Frances Slocum is one of test for the human spirit. This one began on Nov. 2, 1778, at a Pennsylvania homestead during the Revolutionary period. The mother of Frances and most of the family's ten children were in the farm cabin. The father and several of the older children were away at the time.

Late in the afternoon, three Delawares were seen some distance from the cabin. The Slocum mother quickly took the children to a secret place in the nearby woods. Five-year-old Frances, however, had hidden herself under a stairway in the cabin, thinking to play a trick on her mother. The three Delawares found the little girl, grabbed her and started to carry her off.

The mother at this point came running from the woods, screaming for the Indians to drop the child. The Indians simply began to run faster. The last the mother saw of little Frances was her being carried on the shoulder of an Indian disappearing into the forest.

The vision must have been traumatic. The mother spent the rest of her life, 30 years, in the search of the child. During that time, her husband and several of her other children were killed by Indians. The mother never gave up the search. Her instincts made her certain that Frances was alive someplace. This, in spite of the fact she never found Frances or even received any indication of her possible whereabouts.

Before she died, the mother exacted a promise from one of her sons that he would never give up the search for Frances. He kept faith with the mother, traveling over much of the Old Northwest. The son finally found his aging sister Frances in 1837. She was still living along the Mississinewa. The search had covered 59 years.

Chapter 5

The three Shawnee chiefs blinked in the cool January sunlight as they approached the stockade along the banks of the Ohio River at the mouth of a frozen stream.

The Stars and Stripes fluttered over the hastily-built Fort Finney. The Indians hesitated for a moment before approaching the gate. They were the meager representatives of the Indian nations which the United States Government hoped to bind to certain terms -- which amounted to a surrender of a large share of Indian lands north of the Ohio.

But the three chiefs really didn't represent much in the way of Indian power. Weeks before, Little Turtle, the war chief of the Miamis, had met with leaders of the Wea, Piankashaw, Potawatomi, Kickapoo, Huron, Chippewa and Shawnee Indians at Detroit.

"We make no gifts of lands. We recognize no treaties made by the separate tribes of the east. We tell the generals of the United States to give their money to their own people. We will only speak with them when we all speak together, and even then, we give nothing north of the Ohio River."

The Indians generally agreed with Little Turtle. Several of the minor Shawnee chiefs, however, with villages along the lower Miami, decided to give negotiations a try. Like Indians at many other meetings before, they somehow thought if they talked well and long enough, it would make an impression or mean concessions from the Americans.

Inside the fort was Colonel Richard Butler and several peace commissioners of the federal government. The reason the treaty talks were being held at Fort Finney was because the original intended site, Vincennes, was now considered too dangerous. With the increasing hostility of the Indians, there was no safe transport, even those heavily escorted, for either goods or commissioners to the lower Wabash.

But such considerations didn't bother Colonel Butler. He was a short man, a veteran of the Revolution, who always talked in a loud voice. He stared at the Shawnees as they listened to the proposed terms: the Shawnees would acknowledge the U. S. as soverign over all lands ceded by Great Britain (all the Old Northwest); the Americans would hold Indian hostages until the return of all prisoners, and all crimes would be punished by American law.

The three chiefs were stung by the demands. One said: "It is not the custom of the Shawnee to give hostages. We do not understand the measuring out of the lands, it is all ours. You cannot distribute hunting grounds to us that are already ours."

Butler moved forward. "You will accept the terms of the United States Congress or you will be killed. The destruction of your women and children, or their future happiness, depends on your choice. Peace or war are in your power. Make your choice."

The three Shawnee chiefs were cowed. It was typical of negotiations by the Americans at the time. They would force terms from a few chiefs, then claim the treaty applied to all the Indian nations, whether represented or not.

The Shawnees present had reason to fear Butler. He and Colonel Benjamin Logan and George Rogers Clark had led slaughters of Indian villagers many times before and would do so again. Whole areas would be burned out. Indian babies were thrown into fires. Even friendly chiefs were shot down when the heat was on.

Butler was unusual for a regular soldier in that he enjoyed duty in the Indian country. He felt a sense of power over large areas of space and humanity. And there were no restraints. No authorities or civil servants to check back on things.

Colonel Butler was careful to keep a journal of the proceedings, including all his own statements. His threat of "destruction of women and children" seemed to him to be a forceful and suitable way to deal with the savages. The Indians knew enough of Butler to take his threats seriously. They also remembered him. In just five years, Colonel Butler of the Army of the United States would die with a stone ax five inches into his skull.

The crucial era in the Great Lakes Area was fast approaching as a bitter cold winter set in early in the year of 1789. British diplomats at the U. S. Capitol in Philadelphia passed along the information that President George Washington asked and got from Congress a large military appropriation for an expeditionary force against the Indians, and particularly aimed at the destruction of Miamitown.

In the meantime, the Americans built large fortifications at Fort Washington, soon to be called Cincinnati, and further upstream at Marietta. Both of these sites were on the north banks of the Ohio River -- on the Indian side -- and protected rapidly-growing settlements.

Between the British agents in the American capitol and Indians watching every move along the Ohio, Little Turtle learned from day-to-day each movement of the intruders from the east. Trouble was gathering, but the Turtle received assurances and encouragement from the British. The commander at Fort Detroit, Colonel de Peyster, got word to the war chieftain that further supplies of rifles and ammunition would be delivered.

It became clear to the Turtle that the main strike by the Americans would be many moons in the coming. In the meantime, he looked carefully at the two major settlements near the Ohio River forts -- rapidly being increased in size by hundreds of families of Revolutionary War veterans who were given land by the U. S. Congress.

"Send a horseman to Captain Johnny and The Snake," the Turtle said to Le Gris. "Tell them we shall meet on the Little Miami River. They will need to prepare themselves for a party down along the Ohio."

He also told Le Gris to round up several dozen braves for the trip south.

Within days of the meeting, the Shawnees headed by The Snake hit the Marietta settlement under the very guns of Fort Harmar. The Indians walked up the new dirt streets of the town; went into the cabins, killed the men and raped the women. The howls and outrage of the settlers were heard all the way to Philadelphia.

Little Turtle and the Miamis struck Cincinnati, carrying off men, women and children, plus several Negro slaves. Within hours, there flowed out of Fort Washington a force of regulars and Kentucky horsemen. The Turtle, taking his small party north, eluded the pursuers but had to abandon the loot and captives along the banks of the Little Miami. He settled down in the frozen wilderness to await the arrival of Le Gris and a larger group of Miamis and Delawares from the Maumee villages.

But the second attack on Cincinnati and Fort Washington never transpired. With Le Gris came the message that an agent of the British military had arrived at Miamitown and was waiting for talks with the chiefs of the various Indian tribes. Little Turtle took this to be a sign that the British would back him with delivery of large scale gun supplies. It also meant to the Turtle that he would be supported in his Fabian tactics designed to destroy any invading armies by drawing them far into the wilderness -- too far for safe transport of provisions, communications or reinforcements.

When the Turtle arrived back at the three rivers villages, he found a young man named Henry Hay. Hay was both fun-loving and astute. His father was formerly a deputy to Henry Hamilton, the "hair buyer" of frontier notoriety who was commandant at Detroit before de Peyster. Young Hay was doubling up his income by being in the pay of both the British military as an intelligence agent and a large Canadian fur-trading firm as a representative in the territory.

After making his way from Detroit to Miamitown, he wasted no time in establishing several pleasant relationships. He delivered gifts to several of the trading houses, and rum to a few of the Indian chiefs. Within several days, he was also on close terms with the daughters of two French traders' families. In his report to Major Patrick Murray, British regimental commander, Detroit, Hay said he arrived at Miamitown on Dec. 16, 1789. Two days later Indians arrived with white prisoners from the country by the Ohio River. The following day,

33

Dec. 19, the Turtle, Le Gris and a part of their war party arrived.

At this time, the Indians and the British were watching each other and both were watching the Americans. War preparations kindled the frontier wilderness in that winter of 1789.

Little Turtle suggested to Le Gris that it might be well "if our young guest is not out of our sight during his stay here." Le Gris, the tall cadaverous Miami chief, wrapped a figurative Indian blanket around Hay during his three-month stay in Miamitown. It was the sort of winter work Le Gris enjoyed. Let Little Turtle and the others chase across the bleak snowy tracks in the forest hunting grounds. Le Gris preferred the warm, convivial hovels of the semi-civilized Miamitown. And he knew, with a little persuasion, the British agent could be counted on for gallon jugs of rum.

Young Hay gave a day-to-day report to his superiors at Detroit. His observations reflected the war planning of the Indians and the intelligence brought by them concerning the American military movements along the Ohio River. His journal, still in existence today, also indicated the wild sort of time a person could have at these strange crossroads in the interior. Excerpts follow:

Dec. 18, 1789 -- "The Americans are now very busy building redoubts and block houses ever since last summer at Cincinnati. They have three companies of regular Congress troops. The Governor, Arthur St. Clair, is expected down in this place in a short time."

The information was obtained from an American captive. "The Indians who took him are Delawares to learn intelligence of what those people were about." It turned out that the information was very accurate. St. Clair reached Cincinnati within two weeks on Jan. 2, 1790.

Dec. 19 -- "This day arrived here the Little Turtle, a chief of the Miami with his war party. Le Gris ordered a pirogue to be unloaded by some French lads. He billetted the party like soldiers, so many to each house. We had six. This he ordered in a very polite manner, but quite like a general or commandant."

Dec. 21 -- "Captain Johnny, a Shawnee chief arrived,

34

according to a message we sent him the day before. Le Gris introduced me to his son and granddaughter. I was shown the heart of the white prisoner. It was quite dry and fastened to a stick with his scalp. Another party of Miamis and one Shawnee came in. They danced over the river with a scalp flying. They do this sort of thing regularly. It was a rather dirty morning."

Dec. 23 -- "There are two Miami villages in this place. One belongs to Le Gris and the other to Pacan, which in his absence is commanded by Jean Baptiste de Richardville, son of Richardville of Three Rivers, Canada, and an Indian woman. His mother, the sister of Little Turtle, is very clever." (Little Turtle's village was about 20 miles west of Miamitown at Devil's Lake along Eel River in north-central Indiana).

Dec. 24 -- "Potawatomis arrived here this afternoon."

Dec. 25 -- "I cannot say much for the trade in this place. Everyone tries to get what he can by either foul play or otherwise. Mrs. Adamhers gave us some venison steak and roasted raccoon. I played the flute this morning at Mass."

The young British agent wasn't wasting his social hours either that holiday season. He described a series of wild "baches" often after the celebration of Midnight Mass. Once he mentioned his and John Kinzie's finding two comely daughters of French traders with a bottle of rum in a cabin. "The old people were out of the way," Hay said. This Kinzie who made the rounds with Hay was then a young man. Years later he would settle near Fort Dearborn and become known as the father of Chicago.

Dec. 26 -- "Mrs. Le Gris, having made us a present of a very large turkey cock weighing about 30 pounds, we proposed a dinner. Fetched some Madeira, after which Kinzie and I went to see Miss Rivarre and found Miss Adamhers there. The old people were out of the way.

"George Girty arrived here this day from his wintering place only four miles from here. It's called Delaware Town. He said the Miami Indians upbraided the Delawares with telling them the ground they occupied was not theirs. The Delawares said they would be fools to go to war for land not theirs. They will leave the country and go to the Spaniards. Girty asks that his intelligence not be mentioned, but that the British buy off the Delawares to stop them."

Dec. 31 -- "Le Gris and the Turtle breakfasted with us this morning."

Jan. 1, 1790 -- "The Indians are in here in great number, more so indeed than I could ever have thought. Le Gris asked me this morning for a bottle of rum. He was rather drunk towards evening."

While Hay was relaying his intelligence to the English side, the information being passed back and forth among the Americans was oddly different.

"I am persuaded their general confederacy is entirely broken; indeed, it would not be very difficult, if circumstances required it, to set them at deadly variance."

President George Washington received this advice concerning the Indians from General Arthur St. Clair. St. Clair, governor of the Northwest Territory, wrote from his Ohio River headquarters, where he was gathering an army under General Harmar.

But some 200 miles to the northwest, the Indians did not at all appear to be at variance, and if the confederacy was broken, Little Turtle was quickly laying on some patches.

Young Henry Hay, in his report to the commanding officers at Detroit, made clear that warriors from the many tribes below the Great Lakes were gathering at Miamitown far in excess of what the British had believed possible. Within a few more weeks, the agent was to meet many Indian chiefs of the Miami, Shawnee and Wabash Indian tribes. These included Captain Johnny, Blue Jacket, The Snake, Tecumseh, Le Jollie, Tramblai, Porcupine, The Soldier, Black Bears and the King. What part some of these chiefs were to play in the coming battles is as dim as history. Others became well-known figures for several decades. Hay told his superiors that Captain Johnny called a grand council of all the Shawnees. Little Turtle, Le Gris and Pacan were the principal Miami chiefs, though others would play key roles in the crucial events of the next 20 years also. Later, chiefs of the

Ottawas and Chippewas, ancient cousins of the Miamis, would join the Miami Confederation in addition to the Delaware, Huron or Wyandot, Potawatomi, the Illinois, the Mingo and the Kickapoo.

It appears that the intelligence of Governor St. Clair was a bit faulty. The reverse, however, was a different case. Hay's report shows how Little Turtle followed each action of the Americans.

March 21, 1790 -- "They brought three prisoners and a Negro man. They also took 19 prisoners near Limestone. One of the prisoners, named John Witherington, said General St. Clair came down the Ohio. At least 40 souls were taken or killed."

March 23 -- "A Miami arrived last night from Vincennes. There seems to be great want of provisions at the garrison. They are obliged to kill the cattle belonging to the settlers."

March 24 -- "One John Thompson who was taken among the 19 prisoners came here today. He said there was great talk of raising men to come against the Indians." Hay sounds rather casual as he discusses the coming and going of prisoners taken by the Indians down along the Ohio. It is almost as if they were volunteering information about their friends and fellow Americans to the Indians. The realities were quite another thing, even though British records habitually overlooked unpleasantness.

In the meantime, General Harmar was making sweeps along the north banks of the Ohio River in the hopes of surprising the Indian raiding parties. There were few surprises. On one occasion, mounted federal troops caught four fleeing Cherokees and took their scalps back to the fort. The soldiers were annoyed when informed that Cherokees were blood enemies of the Miamis, and hardly the enemy in the developing warfare. On another occasion, six Chippewa warriors, who were among a band which had traveled 600 miles down from north of Lake Huron. were captured.

Toward summer in 1790, the Indians began attacking every settlement from the Mississippi to Pennsylvania and Western New York. While Congress was promising new lands to the citizens of the Thirteen States; the simple truth

37

was, the frontier was moving in the wrong direction. Families were fleeing eastward, many returning to places in Massachusetts and Eastern Virginia, and were giving up on homesteading.

Even military detachments began to travel in convoy fashion for their own protection when coming down the Ohio. In the six years up to this time, the Indians killed more than 1,500 settlers along the Ohio and adjacent lands alone. They also stole 20,000 horses, fired a thousand houses and carried off a large portion of the stores being shipped west from the Eastern Seaboard to support both potential towns and military posts. Cries of anguish to Congress were becoming a political liability and the entire policy of opening the West was in jeopardy.

St. Clair informed President Washington that he planned to wait no longer. He would destroy the Indians and raze Miamitown. General Josiah Harmar would be military leader for the campaign.

In one last conversation with an envoy of St. Clair, Little Turtle spoke in an odd prophetic way, saying: "We meet; I cut him down; and his shade, as it passes on the wind, shuns my walk."

Chapter 6

It was a quiet dry morning in early October and the maple leaves were just beginning to turn along the shores of Lake Erie. Little Turtle walked his horse along the sandy beach to the mouth of the Maumee and stopped at a spot where today the piers for the port of Toledo handle foreign cargo.

He too was counting foreign imports on that day in 1790 -- shipments of rifles which had originated at Liverpool beyond the great sea.

The Miami chief, who seldom displayed anything but an easy calm, was rather distracted on this particular occasion. An American army -- he wasn't quite sure of the size -- was moving north. The pipelines of the wilderness, plus generous intelligence from British agents, told the Indian chieftain this army was headed for Miamitown at the confluence of the three rivers. And the army, which had left Fort Washington on the Ohio River a week earlier, was moving faster than expected. Little Turtle was in a hurry to have the guns moved up river the 90 miles. To save time, he distributed the supplies on the spot to a collection of Miami, Delaware and Shawnee braves. He then proceeded alone on horseback along the back trails which wound their way to the north of the river route.

At a village near the Auglaize River, he was told the army had crossed the Miami River and was continuing north toward Girty Town and the St. Mary's River. The Kickapoo and Shawnee warriors were harassing the American forces according to plans set by the Indians weeks earlier. Any trains of provisions from Cincinnati were to be raided. Foraging parties and scouts were to be killed or captured. It was the Turtle's idea to isolate the invaders in every way possible.

Later in that same day, Little Turtle learned a piece of unsettling information. It came from a captive Kentucky militiaman, a hard red-eyed man in his forties taken by a party of Kickapoo. A second force of Americans, some 330 riflemen, were on their way from Vincennes to join the regular army in a pincer movement against Miamitown.

The army of General Harmar had begun its march from Cincinnati during the last week in September. The force, the largest American military effort to that date to be launched into the Indian country, totaled 1,453 men. There were also a number of women and a few children who had attached themselves to the force. The army consisted of 320 regular federal troops and 1,133 militia, mostly from Pennsylvania and Kentucky.

Some of the officers included Maj. James Wyllys of the regulars, Maj. James Fontaine of the mounted Kentucky riflemen, Col. John Hardin of the Kentucky militia and Capt. William Ferguson, who was in charge of an artillery company which was hauling three brass cannons through the wilderness.

Little Turtle learned more quickly than General Harmar that the force of 300 troops from Vincennes under Maj. John Hamtramck had turned back to their fort on the lower Wabash. Because of a shortage of provisions, many of Hamtramck's men had refused to continue up river. Thus the warchief had only to be concerned with the 1,453-man army of General Harmar -- a force somewhat larger in numbers than the 1,000 Indian braves the Turtle had available for the coming meeting at Miamitown.

On the evening of Oct. 14, an Indian scouting party came quickly into the main Indian village at the northeast junction of the Maumee and St. Joseph Rivers. They told Little Turtle that a mounted force of some 800 soldiers and militia was making a dash for Miamitown in an attempt to hit the Indians in a surprise move.

The Turtle began immediately to vacate the Miami villages, including the secreting of stores of the traders in selected spots in the area. All was deserted. The buildings were set afire.

As the sun came up the next morning, Little Turtle watched from a small hill near the St. Joseph River. Coming into view on the south side of the Maumee were the troops of Colonel Hardin. Smoke from the smouldering ruins of the villages partially obscured the soldiers as they started to cross the stream.

The Turtle withdrew some distance to the north. He had in mind to give the Americans some time to themselves. Let them have their fun. He had time. And he was sure, given time, someone would make mistakes.

Three fat Delaware squaws were leading and dragging their limited domestic possessions across the grassy hillside as Little Turtle's war party passed to the east. Smoke from the Shawnee villages along the Maumee -- just west of where New Haven, Indiana, is now located -- could be seen above the trees as the Indians approached. But the incendiary patrols of Colonel Hardin had already departed, and had slipped back the few miles to the American encampment at burnt-out Miamitown.

It was the second day since the invasion of the villages by the advance forces of the federal army. Later in the day, the main body of men under General Harmar began emerging from the wooded south shore of the Maumee; crossed the river and began to settle in a protected position in the open area of Miamitown.

The Indians kept their distance as they continued to watch the Americans put the torch to the villages in the vicinity. While the Miamis themselves had emptied and burned their own villages and store houses at the immediate three rivers area, the soldiers were busy with others nearby. They leveled two Delaware villages several miles up the St. Mary's River and another village north a few miles along the St. Joseph. More than 100 houses were razed, the corn burned out and any stray livestock grabbed.

Mostly, the soldiers found precious little worth taking, and saw only an occasional defiant Indian, who immediately drew a cascade of pot shots. Since the prime objective of the invasion was to punish the Indians, the army began to show signs of frustration after another day at the river fork and nothing in hand to assault.

Wetting this frustration was the intention of Little

Turtle, whose main occupation at this point was to repress the almost constant inclination of young braves to make headlong assaults at the army position. The Miami warchief waited one more day.

In the pink early light of October 19, the Indians noticed a stir in the army camp. Soon, a column of men, about 300, began to file out to the west. The Turtle guessed the Americans had received information concerning Miami villages and French trading houses some 20 miles to the west along Eel River. He waved a war party of about 200 Indians in the same direction. The main body of warriors he left along the St. Joseph River Bank, close enough for the dependable Le Gris to keep his one eye focused on the American camp.

The Indians were picking their way along the chill edge of a swamp when it became apparent that some of the soldiers were no longer with the marauding column. A little later, a company of horsemen left -- supposedly to seek out a straggling portion of the patrol. The remaining foot soldiers, something like 120 men among the thickets along Eel River, could be seen staring into the trees as they heard some rifle shots in the distance.

Within minutes, the Indians materialized right in front of their eyes. Little Turtle's braves fired rifles at point blank range and went in on top of the Americans with rifle butts and iron axes. The soldiers, mostly regulars from Pennsylvania, retreated at a dead run to the east. The Indians followed several into the thickets and swamps, where a number on both sides were killed; and where a few of the soldiers survived by hiding in the mucky water. About 60 of the federal force died in the skirmish where U. S. Highway 33 now crosses the Eel River, about the midway between Columbia City and Churubusco, Indiana.

As night approached, Little Turtle could hear the cannons of General Harmar firing at Miamitown. The purpose of the noise was to signal the direction of the encampment to any soldiers lost in the forested vicinity. Very few returned during the dark hours.

Little Turtle and Le Gris were in parley the next day with The Snake and Blue Jacket of the Shawnees (Captain Punk of the Delawares had been killed the day before when he tried to steal a horse along the Maumee). The Turtle convinced the other chiefs of the advantages of continuing to wait for the Americans to send out new raiding parties. He said any frontal attacks across the cleared land at Miamitown would be a "bloody faux pas."

He was completely surprised the following morning by a report that General Harmar was packing up his entire army and vacating Miamitown.

Chief Le Gris and The Snake stood in the middle of the burned rubble of Miamitown and told a gathering of squaws and boys to prepare for a huge bonfire. Le Gris then passed to The Snake a large earthenware jug of rum.

The repulsed army of the United States was by now several hours to the south. There was time for a celebration before taking up the chase.

The spirits of the black October night were undampened by a steady chill drizzle. Dancing and shouts drew increasing numbers around the fire, including Potawatomi and Kickapoo warriors who had come from afar, apparently too late to join the battle against the troops of General Josiah Harmar.

Little Turtle sat at one end of a large semi-circle of chiefs of the Miami, Shawnee, Delaware, Potawatomi and Kickapoo tribes. Old Le Gris, standing in bony tall silhouette by the fire, suddenly threw a large jar of rum into the flames. As a flare of light and sound went up, he emitted a drunken guttural laugh: "There goes the enemy of the Miami."

As the night wore on, the various chiefs spoke louder of taking up the trail of the retreating army. From time-to-time they would look in the direction of the Turtle; but, he continued to look into the fire and did not speak. A little later, he went to a shelter which the squaws had been setting up and went to sleep.

The touch of a young Indian woman awoke Little Turtle. A dog barked in the distance. It was about an hour before dawn on Oct. 22, 1790.

The Miami warchief held a cup of hot soup between his hands as he walked toward the Maumee River. Already

43

standing on the bank of the stream was Le Gris, tall with an ancient buffalo hide hanging from his shoulders. Le Gris was staring across the water, looking silently to the south.

The soldiers were coming back. During the night, a backwoodsman named David Williams had informed General Harmar and Colonels Hardin and Fontaine that the Indians were back in Miamitown. The Americans, about 10 miles south of the villages (where the town of Hoagland is today), decided on a sudden last stroke to punish the savages. Hardin, Fontaine and Maj. John Wyllys were named to head the rapid march of 340 mounted riflemen and 60 federal regulars.

The clammy mist had cleared during the night and the first glimmering of the morning sun was in the east when Little Turtle heard horses in the woods across the Maumee. Concealed with the chieftain near the north bank were more than 600 Miami and confederate braves, mostly armed with flintlocks.

But instead of coming across the river to Miamitown, as the Turtle had expected, the American horsemen could be heard swinging to the west. They were going around the Maumee bend and across the St. Mary's River. Soon, part of the American force could be seen riding swiftly up the bank on the far side of the river and going north along the St. Joseph. This would put them to the rear of the Indian position. Little Turtle sent a small portion of his party to follow the mounted riflemen. "Keep them always in your vision," he warned.

In but a short time, the Turtle could hear guns firing to the rear -- along the St. Joseph. He motioned for the Indians concealed along the Maumee, however, to stay put. He had learned by this time that a company of soldiers had remained in the woods on the opposite side of the Maumee. He knew they would also hear the shots. He wondered what they would do.

Minutes later, the Miami chief could see the U. S. regulars under Major Wyllys begin to stream into the river, holding their rifles high as they waded in the hip-deep water.

All the while, popping sounds of the flintlock rifles increased in the distance. The Turtle could tell from the sound that both the Indians and the mounted Kentucky and Pennsylvania militia were skirmishing about a half-mile north along the St. Joseph. But the Indians at the Maumee brush remained silent.

When the federal troops reached midstream, the warriors under the Turtle opened fire -- shooting their rifles in rapid fashion, then picking up other rifles on the ready and firing them. The whithering ambush struck down nearly the entire floundering troop within moments. Only a handful of soldiers managed to scramble up the slick clay bank of the opposite side and escape south.

In the meantime, The Snake had been drawing the mounted riflemen of Colonels Fontaine and Hardin further north along the St. Joseph. As the American horsemen spread out, the Indians would attack. When the Americans drew together for an assault, the Indians would run again. At a constricted moment in this elastic sort of activity, The Snake saw Colonel Fontaine shot from his horse. He slipped quickly to the spot and cut off the scalp from the not-yet-dead officer.

Upon hearing the heavy firing of rifles along the Maumee (where Little Turtle's guns were cutting down Major Wyllys and his regulars), the mounted riflemen swung around in that direction. They came riding up to the rear of the Miamis, and the Indians ducked for cover in all directions. But the Americans did not stop. They rode swiftly through the Indians and crossed the river, joining the fleeing remnant of the regulars.

Several miles south of the Maumee, the retreating forces were met by some reenforcements, who had been coming to join the battle. Now, however, these too turned around and returned with the others to the encampment of General Harmar.

A small party of Indians headed by Le Gris followed cautiously in the wake of the retreat. Late in the afternoon the old chief, with his one eye cocked, lifted his head above a decaying oak stump. He could see the camp of General Harmar and its constricted borders -- heavily guarded. Harmar had lost 181 men killed in the fighting at Miamitown. Added to that were the stragglers caught by the Indians along the route of the campaign, which brought the total losses to more than 200 men out of his army of 1,453. The Northwest wilderness was becoming more forbidding by the hour. Supplies were growing short and the hurrying grey clouds overhead threw a chill over the aging Revolutionary War veteran.

Le Gris and his party kept a watch on the encampment through the night. At daybreak, they could see the Americans working at their pack animals and filling the wagons. The army soon began the move south -- back to the Ohio River and Fort Washington at Cincinnati.

Despite the many dead, the Indians saw the repulse of Harmar's army as a great victory. The reputation of Little Turtle as a military leader spread a thousand miles across the frontierland and beyond. To the end of his life, he would be habitually called the Great Little Turtle. In future battles, larger numbers of warriors would come greater distances to be a part of the Miami chieftain's forces.

Sitting on an oaken bench against the wall of a log building the night after Harmar's departure, the Turtle told several Indian leaders and an agent of the British of his own vision of the battle at the present site of Fort Wayne.

"The soldiers came and we defeated them. They wanted to build a fort in our chief town, and they could not. We would not let them supply it. We would not let them hold it.

They had to go back from the Indian lands to save themselves. Now we can bury our braves and return to our own villages."

Strategically, the victory of the Miami Confederacy had been complete. The tactics of Little Turtle in isolating the invading army and attacking its smaller parts were effective. General Arthur St. Clair, the United States Congress and President Washington soon were aware they had no more control of the area northwest of the Ohio River than before. As winter snow swept down from the Great Lakes, the Indians remained lords of the wilderness.

Chapter 7

Bear, bobcat, beaver, deer and raccoon, plus wolves, fox and mink are what Indian braves had in front of their eyes during the long dark winter days in the Northwest Territory 180 years ago.

After the retreat of the American army back to the Ohio River, hunting parties tracked through the snow of the forests, which extended from the great black swamp south of the Maumee River to Lake Michigan and Lake Huron. Furs were the main business of the Miami and other Indians in the area. Meat from the game animals was the crucial item on village tables, especially in the winter of 1790-91 because a large part of the corn crop had been destroyed by General Josiah Harmar and his troops.

Little Turtle headed northwest from his village along the Eel River. Winter came early that season and the frost was already deep into the earth. A flock of wild turkeys flushed noisily from a copse of bushes as the Turtle and his party came to the shore of Lake Wawasee.

The Indians crossed on the ice of the lake and continued to Little Turtle's ancestorial home along the St. Joseph of the Lake River, near where South Bend is now located, upstream from Lake Michigan. It was the village of his grandfather. His father, who had died about 15 years earlier, was born here. In more recent years, Potawatomi Indians had established villages in the vicinity.

The Miami Indians claimed all the land from the shores of Lake Michigan to the shores of Lake Erie, south to the Ohio River. Most of the other tribes, which were migrating into the Miami lands, recognized the Miami claims and felt safe in establishing their homes there. The Potawatomis, however, were somewhat belligerent about Miami land ownership and took the attitude that what they could hold was theirs.

It was not Little Turtle's intention on this trip to make a point about the land. The Potawatomis were among the

47

most hostile anti-American tribes. They were more numerous than the Miami. They would be needed.

Immediately after the Indian victory in October, Little Turtle had hoped the United States would be discouraged about seeking lands north of the Ohio River. Soon, however, emissaries of the Americans appeared in the Indian villages, attempting to gain concessions from some of the chiefs. Apparently hoping, they were, to take with words what they had failed to do with muscle. Several of these emissaries were killed by the Indians. Others were sent back before they traveled far into the hostile lands.

Little Turtle refused to talk with the American delegates. "They do not come to talk or agree. They come to get something that we will not give. They come and threaten our people."

As it became more obvious that the Indians were not through with incursions by armed American forces, the Turtle decided he needed all the allies he could get, including the Potawatomis. He also visited Indian settlements at the present location of Chicago, which is but slightly changed from its Miami Indian name of Chikago, and villages along the Wabash. The Indian towns were more crowded than ever, but there was a wet chill in the air.

When the news of Harmar's defeat finally sunk into the political attitudes of the American Capitol, it amounted to a serious liability in the Administration of President Washington. Representatives of frontier areas were screaming for protection. The spectacle of U. S. regulars being forced to turn tail by "motley savages" was too much to bear.

Late in March, as the ice thawed along the Maumee, there arrived in Miamitown an agent of the British military. He told Little Turtle of a report from a British diplomat in Philadelphia that on March 3, 1791, the U. S. Congress has passed legislation calling for a new deployment along the frontier. The army was to number 3,000 men and was to be under the command of General Arthur St. Clair.

President Washington passed along instructions to Secretary of War Henry Knox. The instructions, forwarded to General St. Clair, said:

"You will proceed vigorously, and every preparation in your power, for the purpose of the main expedition; and having assembled your force, and all things in readiness .. you will commence your march for the Miami villages, in order to establish a strong and permanent military post at that place. In your advance you will establish post of communication with Fort Washington (Cincinnati). The post at the Miami village is intended for awing and curbing the Indians .. and afford a detachment of five or six hundred men, either to chastise any of the Wabash or other hostile Indians and secure any convoy of provisions. With the whole of your force, you will use every exertion to make them feel the effects of your superiority .. You will seek the enemy and strike them with great severity."

Though the main army of the new nation was to be employed, the attitude of the government still indicated the campaign was to be in the nature of a punitive expedition. Little real knowledge of the enemy is expressed. Apparently, no one had yet taken the pains to determine the name of the leader of the Indians, or how many warriors he had at his disposal. But the rather slight warchief with the long straight black hair was going his quiet way in the river and forest lands. He knew fresh invasions were coming, and wasn't especially surprised when they came along a route never used by the Americans before.

Rain came in torrents, sweeping across the Wabash, as Little Turtle and his party hurried toward Ouiatenon (near present-day Lafayette, Indiana).

The Miami chieftain had chosen to travel on foot through the forests along the river in the search for the American raiding force under General Charles Scott. It was the Turtle's opinion that lightly-clad men on foot had an advantage in the bogs and thick woods over horsemen.

The Indians moved at a change of pace -- walking, running then resting. The Turtle knew the 850-man cavalry troop of Kentucky riflemen already had a two-day head start. He also knew his only chance of catching the horsemen would be if they decided to turn back to hit one more Indian village, or stopped for awhile for the weather to improve.

At the point where the Eel River joins the Wabash, the Turtle and his party met The Soldier, a Wea chief, and a scattering of the Wabash Indians. The area was desolate, in spite of it being the first week in June.

The Soldier told Little Turtle the American cavalry had first attacked Ouiatenon, firing on everything that moved, then proceeded across the river to set fire to the Kickapoo villages a few miles further west.

Part of the troop -- some 350 of the Kentuckians -- went by night on foot further up the Wabash for a surprise raid on the Eel River villages. Most of the Indians escaped by swimming the rain-swollen river, as soldiers fired volleys after them.

Little Turtle decided to continue on to Ouiatenon to take up the trail from there, even though he knew General Scott's troops had departed and were believed headed southeast. In the meantime, he sent Indian runners in scattered patterns to seek the whereabouts of the enemy. The Miami warchief was further expecting some 500 Potawatomi warriors to join the hunt.

It was under the orders of General St. Clair at Cincinnati that Scott and his men gathered south of the Ohio River to ready themselves for the campaign. They moved across the river on May 23 and went at horse-killing speed through the hills, streams and valleys of southern Indiana in an effort to take the Wabash Indians by surprise. They were successful, partly because of the rapidity of the effort and the almost continuous thunderstorms which kept the Indians under cover and washing away the traces of their movements.

After hitting the Wabash Indians, Scott and his men headed straight for the safety of Fort Washington along the Ohio. Little Turtle had picked up the trail at Ouiatenon and for three days dogged the hoof marks of the 850-man troop. But the Indians were never able to close the distance. Scott had killed 32 braves and took 58 prisoners

50

in the raids on the Wabash villages. They were mostly women and children who would be kept as hostages. He did not lose a single man. The destroyed town of Ouiatenon was never rebuilt. It was the end of a major post built a century before by the French, and for a long time a key trading post and gathering place for the   Indians.   So complete was the razing of the fort and surrounding structures that the exact location is uncertain today.

The Scott attack was the opening blow in the campaign of General St. Clair to destroy the power of the Miami Confederacy and assume control of the Indian lands of the Old Northwest. The aim of the Scott expedition was to keep the Indians off balance. The main attack by the army of more than 2,000 men was to come later in the season.

So successful was the Scott raid that St. Clair decided on another hit-and-run attack. On August 1, 1791, Colonel James Wilkinson led 500 mounted men out of Cincinnati and headed north. Where Scott had taken a northwest course through the hills and across the White River to reach the Wabash villages, Wilkinson went straight up the approximate route of General Harmar the previous year. In rapid movements, Wilkinson traveled as far as the portage between the Great Miami and St. Mary's River, acting as if he intended to hit Miamitown further north along the Maumee. Suddenly, however, his troops cut sharply to the left and headed on a westerly course below the Miami villages and toward the same Wabash villages hit two months before by Scott. Wilkinson captured the Wea Chief Little Face, cut down any Indians who had attempted to move back to the area and burned anything rebuilt or still standing in the river area. He then retreated rapidly to the Ohio River over the same route as Scott.

"We shall not be fooled again," said Little Turtle at the edge of the great Blank Swamp which covered a thousand square miles south of the Maumee in those days. The Turtle, together with The Snake and other Shawnees, had failed to make contact with Wilkinson's horsemen, missing them by several hours in the wilderness when the Americans turned suddenly west.

"Never again do the Miamis wait for the soldiers to

51

come to our villages. We shall watch them at the great river and in their every step. And when they come, all the Indian nations will gather here on the land south of the Black Swamp. We will see if they get so easily away on another day," said the Turtle. Two months later, the day had arrived.

Little Turtle looked up and could see scant clouds drifting across the otherwise clear sky. The first evening stars were already making their appearance; while all around him the light from a hundred fires flickered among the trees.

The Miami warchief had already decided. On the following morning, the vast host of the Miami Confederacy would attack the army of General Arthur St. Clair. The Americans had for many weeks been working their way up from the Ohio River. By this time they had set up camp along an upper stream of the Wabash, a site where Fort Recovery, Ohio, is located today.

The Turtle was his usual calm self, in spite of the coming action and the fact that he now headed the largest Indian army he had ever seen or even heard about. Everything was as he had hoped. The British had delivered the guns and ammunition in quantity. The rifles and supplies had been transported in flatboats across Lake Erie and up the Maumee to Miamitown.

Indians from the far reaches of the Great Lakes had streamed south for the coming meeting with the new army of the United States. The Huron, the Ottawa and the Chippewa, who had been encouraged by both Little Turtle and the agents of the British commandant at Detroit, had come hundreds of miles along the streams, lakes and Indian trails. They joined the Miami, the Shawnee, the Delaware, the Potawatomi, the Kickapoo and the Mingo in a great rendezvous on the high ground near Vaughn Creek, not far from where U. S. Highway 27 even today follows the old Indian route. From there, the Indians had taken up their guns and moved south as far as a small branch of the Salamonie River. This was thick forest land some five miles west of the American encampment.

Little Turtle could smell the strong fragrance of decaying walnuts as he studied the scene. Through the trees came the loud voices of Simon Girty and Matthew Elliott, American renegades who worked as agents for the British in the dirty underside of that trade. They were arguing with several Delaware and Shawnee chiefs over the provisions brought overland from Miamitown and how those items were to be shared.

Approaching The Turtle were Chief Le Gris and a tall young Shawnee chief. It amused the Miami chief to see the contrast in the two men. Le Gris, ancient and dour with one eye and a crippled ankle, yet with a complete grasp of those things which go into winning battles, and the young Shawnee Tecumseh, bronze and eager with two rifles, a flintlock pistol and an iron ax strapped to his sides.

Tecumseh had been heading a party of Indians which had been tracking the American army ever since it marched from Fort Washington along the Ohio on Sept. 17, 1791. Tecumseh, and other raiders under The Snake of the Shawnees and Buckongehelas of the Delawares, had been constantly harassing the slow-moving army of St. Clair, grabbing supplies and horses, picking off stragglers.

"The entire army counts more than 2,000 soldiers," said Tecumseh to the Turtle, "but there are less than that with their commander now."

The Miami warchief listened again to a recount of the progress of General St. Clair's forces up to that moment. The Americans had first erected a stockade, Fort Hamilton, about 25 miles north of Cincinnati. Next, continuing along the same line of march, they built Fort St. Clair some 20 miles upstream along the Miami River. Still further north, Fort Jefferson was constructed several miles short of the present town of Greenville, Ohio. From there, the army marched to their encampment which was under the careful observation of Little Turtle's gathering warriors.

"We see them leave men to guard each fort. This afternoon, we take two men and a woman along the river. We get information from them," Tecumseh said with a smile about the mouth, but not the eyes:

"They tell us many of the Kentucky soldiers run away,

back to the fort. They tell us a company of regular soldiers go after them. We follow and it is true. With the general now are no more than 1,500 soldiers."

Little Turtle looked at his watch. He had learned to appreciate the usefulness of British time pieces as well as their guns. The Indians under the Turtle did not go to war with bows and arrows.

The Miami warchief turned to Le Gris, waving his arm over a wide arc. "Tell them all, we go now."

Within the camp of General Arthur St. Clair there was an acrimonious air.

It was not basically due to the poor discipline of the Kentucky horsemen and other frontier rustics. That was the typical condition of all the armies which operated in the border territories. Nor was it because of the several hundred camp followers who had attached themselves to the American forces. In some ways, they were useful in long campaigns.

The trouble was deep, and had existed before the army began its march north. It was a conflict between two men -- the commander and the second-in-command who thought he should have been the commander.

Arthur St. Clair, born in Scotland and educated at Edinburgh, was a descendant of the Earl of Orkney. He was a man of refined manners and large imposing appearance who became an American general in the Revolution. In a technical sense, he served as a first president of the United States -- as president of the Constitutional Assembly of the 13 colonies until the election of George Washington in 1789 following the approval of the Constitution. St. Clair saw the Indians as near subhumans and the frontiersmen as half-civilized types to be kept at arms length. He was not exactly at home with foul Indian campaigning.

Maj. Gen. Richard Butler, the second in command, was a veteran of the frontier wars. From childhood in Pennsylvania, he had scratched his way over other men. He had been a division commander under Anthony Wayne during the Revolution. He was at this time one of the most feared soldiers in the old Northwest. He was short in stature and sure of himself, and insensitive to human considerations, save any slight to himself. He had a bull-horn voice and enjoyed cowing the Indians during the so-called peace talks. Butler regularly told the various chiefs their women and children would likely be destroyed unless they agreed to terms. He sent companies into Indian villages to prove his point. Unlike St. Clair, Butler was no stranger to the Miami and Shawnee tribes.

Butler had made it so obvious that he thought St. Clair was bungling the campaign, the two men were no longer speaking to each other by the time the army reached its wilderness encampment -- which St. Clair planned to use as a jumping off place for his sweep to Miamitown. Colonel Winthrop Sargent, an old Revolutionary soldier, was acting as go-between for the two antagonistic general officers.

It was St. Clair who ordered a regiment under Colonel John Hamtramck to go after a group of militia which, growing wary of the Indian country, had deserted south. "If you had hung a few of them earlier, this would have never happened," Butler said with obvious contempt.

The odd troop movements of the Americans had been observed by Tecumseh and his scouting party. Now, at the stream in the wilderness, the advance party of the Indian confederation carefully moved among the dense foliage. Generally, they slipped from the west, around the north side of the encampment of the federal army.

During the night, heavy cloud cover moved in from the northwest. There was absolute darkness among the trees and the feeling of snow in the air.

Several hours before dawn, Little Turtle and Le Gris were close enough to see the numerous campfires which dotted the outer rim of a clearing made by the invaders the previous day. A little later, about 400 yards across the stream from the tent of General St. Clair, there was a quiet movement among the trees.

"We can remain here now," said Little Turtle. He had already walked slowly around the entire army position.

He had seen numerous sentries and a series of log embattlements at the edges of most of the camp.

The main army was on the east side of the stream. On the other side of the water was the militia -- possibly 200 yards from the position of the regulars. It was at this place -- the encampment of the militia -- that the Indians could make their first strike, the Turtle decided.

"Tell your warriors to use only rifles to flush the Americans on this side of the river," Little Turtle said quietly to several chiefs. "This will drive them into the water and to the other side. Then, if the soldiers come at us here, we will move back. Let them come as far as they will." The warchief then moved away into the night.

Coming upon Le Gris, the warchieftain said "Go to Blue Jacket and tell him we will wait until the sun rises. And stay with him. See that he waits until the soldiers turn their backs and come this way."

The Turtle had long before noticed that sentries often relax and think of their stomachs when the darkness fades with the coming of morning light. He was also aware that men set aside their weapons when they sit down to a meal.

In the surrounding of the army of General St. Clair, the Miami chief positioned the Indians at two main points -- to the west where he himself was now concealed in heavy natural growth and to the northeast where a force under Blue Jacket was hidden.

The Turtle reasoned that rifle fire from the Indians on the west would send the militia fleeing across the stream to where the main army of the Americans was encamped. The militia, on the west side of the tributary of the upper Wabash, numbered about 700 men, mostly from Kentucky. The date was Nov. 4, 1791, and the site was the western edge of present-day Ohio.

As he sat quietly on a frosty log, Little Turtle could feel the stillness of the night fade and the daytime life of the forest begin to take its place. The squawking of a thousand birds increased with each new ray of dawn light. Shortly, a gentle breeze carried the odor of frying ox fat from the nearby army.

Little Turtle had some 2,500 warriors at his command, with more than half of that number in the bushes and behind the trees around the federal army. The Indians had been standing for several hours with cold metal weapons in their hands. Lean and only partly clad in the fashion of the Miamis, they were not waiting for breakfast. They made no fires, and only an ear tuned to the music of the wilderness could tell the stillness was not quite natural.

The almost simultaneous fire from several hundred flintlocks broke the morning calm and hit into the militia. The Turtle could see men going for their rifles and diving for the ground. Others were stumbling in cavant surprise, falling backwards into tents and over bedrolls. A miniball whistled past the Turtle's head, one of several fired in the direction of the smoke puffs coming from the guns of the Indians.

Mostly, however, there was a turmoil of confusion in the militia camp. First a few ducked into the stream and crossed to the east side. Soon, there was a mass movement in that direction -- toward the position of the regular army.

As the militia went stumbling through the first line of the federal troops, the regulars began answering the Indian fire. After several minutes, a command shout could be heard and the regulars came across the stream in a rapid run at Little Turtle and the Indians. The warriors immediately stopped firing and, ducking and running, slipped deeper into the woods.

The Miami chief had been hoping the entire main army would turn its guns in his direction, after the flushing of the men of the militia. Drawing the fire of the regulars, and getting them out of their protected disposition, would give Blue Jacket's warriors an opportunity to move unnoticed and attack St. Clair's army from the other side.

This ruse was only partially successful. The first line of the American troops came at the Indians. But the second line, under General Butler, stayed in position, protecting the regular army camp and artillery, which had commenced to blast grape shot into the trees.

As he went deeper into the brush, the Turtle could no longer see the action at the camp. His immediate effort was the flanking of the onrushing troops. These movements were thwarted, however, when the regulars halted and took up protected placements behind trees and continued regular fire at the Indians.

It was at this time that Little Turtle heard a sudden flurry of rifle shots in the distance. The Indian warriors under Blue Jacket and Le Gris were attacking the federal army to the east.

Old Le Gris, ancient and hereditary chief of the Kekionga branch of the Miamis, was about the only Indian dressed for the weather in the campaign against the army of the American generals.

As he sat hunched under a huge buffalo hide, his one eye had stared fixedly through the brush at the sudden storm of activity of the U. S. troops on both sides of the upper Wabash. When Little Turtle and the Indians on the other side of the stream opened fire on the militia, Le Gris reached forward and put a staying hand on the back of Blue Jacket, the Shawnee chief.

"We wait still," he said in a hoarse whisper. One of Little Turtle's tactical problems in battle was the restraining of the natural impulsive characteristics of the Indians. His best instrument in holding back warriors from premature actions was Le Gris, who was held in a fear almost bordering on superstition by many of the other Indians.

Le Gris and Blue Jacket could see from their concealed spot to the northwest of St. Clair's army that the battle was developing rapidly. The militia, driven from a camp on the west side of the stream, were watched with nervous eagerness as they came splashing through the water to the regular army position. Soon, hundreds of federal troops moved toward the stream and across, driving at the Indians who were in the woods to the west.

But not all the soldiers turned toward the firing, which would have left their backs to the warriors under Blue Jacket. Directly in front of the still concealed Indians was the large group of regulars under General Butler. It was this force which Le Gris continued to hold in his gaze.

Soon, it became apparent that the other American soldiers were not following the warriors of Little Turtle very far into the forest, and might soon return to rejoin the troops in the encampment. Le Gris rose up from the foliage.

"Maintenant, maintenant," he said guttural French to Blue Jacket, who immediately gave a heart-arresting yell.

Nearly a thousand half-naked Indians materialized out of the forest, some no more than 20 feet from the outmost soldiers. There was an immediate exchange of rifle fire; and when the smoke cleared, the battle was hand-to-hand. Indians were swinging gun butts at soldiers who were thrusting with bayonets.

One of the first positions hit by the Indians was the cannon emplacement. Soon, however, mounted soldiers slashing with swords drove the Indians from the large guns.

It was near this spot that Le Gris sighted General Butler, who was struggling with his mount and swinging at an Indian underhoof. Le Gris saw blood streaming from Butler's thigh. A bullet had hit the general's leg and also did some damage to the horse.

The old Miami chief bounded from his concealment and grabbed at Butler's tunic, trying to pull him from the saddle. Butler, however, brought the hilt of his sword around in a vicious swipe, catching Le Gris in the side of the head.

Nearly blinded by the blow, the old Indian held on and then kicked at the underside of the horse, which reared up, sending both men to the ground.

Butler, already crippled by the gunshot in the leg, rolled over with instantaneous exertion and hammered his sword blade into the shoulder of Le Gris. It was his last act.

Le Gris, with his other arm, brought down a large stone ax which crashed into the forehead of the American general. The old chief then straightened up, tall and ashen faced. He looked around, but found he was practically sightless. With a shocking impact on his spine, a horseman crashed him down to the ground again. The old Indian arose once more. After a moment, he found an American tent. It was empty. He went in and sat down on

59

an officer's field chair, while the general melee raged all around.

The army of General St. Clair constricted quickly after the two-sided attack. Little Turtle could see some hand-to-hand combat on the far side of the compound; but mostly, the battle had settled down to a rifle fire exchange. The soldiers were concentrated in the cleared area by the stream. The Indians of the Miami Confederacy were in the surrounding woods.

The sounds of the guns were ringing continuously in his ears as the Miami warchief worked his way through the trees to the south of the perimeter. While stepping quickly through the chill water of the stream, the Turtle came upon two buckboard wagons of provisions.

But others had already taken advantage of the supply wagons. Simon Girty, The Snake and several of the Shawnee warriors were tearing at the bundles of American material. One of the army teamsters was lying face down and partially submerged at the edge of the waterway. The other had apparently made his escape.

Little Turtle was annoyed to see that the dead man had been scalped. He had no objection to the scalping of enemy soldiers, as the practice was both common and profitable. A scalp was sure evidence of an enemy killed in battle and a thing to bring a reward. But the Turtle had little tolerance with warriors who quit the battle for such activities, or, who made premature grabs at the war booty.

"Come with me now," he said to The Snake. It was the Miami chief's intention to strengthen the surrounding of the American army of some 1,500 soldiers. He was beginning to envision the possibility of a complete annihilation of the invading force.

Just as the group of Indians turned to join a party approaching from the east, around from the other side, a large troop of horsemen came splashing toward them along the stream. As the Indians scattered into the trees, Little Turtle could see General St. Clair, red-faced and agitated, yelling some instructions over his shoulder. At that moment, several shots hit into the side of the general's

60

horse, and St. Clair went sideways into the water.

But before the Indians could take any action, another horseman brought up a new mount. The general, apparently unhurt, lifted himself into the saddle and moved on as more of the cavalry continued down the stream, and then to the higher land to the south.

Several minutes later, the mounted troops came back quickly toward the main encampment. The Turtle knew instinctively that the American army was preparing a route of retreat. He was sure at that moment the Indians had won a great victory.

The soldiers at the encampment were too concentrated to either take effective counter action or to protect themselves from the volleys of rifle shot which continued to strike into the center from surrounding wilderness. After about an hour, even the distribution of ammunition became deadly work, then nonexistent.

St. Clair was attempting to get his army moving south to safety in an orderly manner. Several companies of regulars moved out first and flushed a number of braves in the brush as they proceeded. But soon, some of the troops broke into a run. They were joined by a rush of militiamen. Fear augmented fear. The retreat began to take on the look of a general rout.

Again Little Turtle saw General St. Clair, who was on still another horse. The general and several other officers were lashing out at men who were trying to duck by in a dash to save their necks. One of the officers swung around with a pistol and put a bullet in the back of one of the runaways.

There was no way for the Indians to stop the mass movement south -- toward the safety of Fort Jefferson, some 29 miles distant. Little Turtle, however motioned to parties of Miami, Mingo and Potawatomi warriors. They would dog the path of the Americans. Any of the slow, the tired, the injured or the weak would fall prey to the Indians. So great was fear, that several men made it the entire 29 miles with leg bones shattered to a degree that they normally would have been unable to take two steps. One went most of the way on a stump, his ankle and foot trailing behind. Among those dragged down from behind were a number of women who were with the army. Many of the wounded fell quickly enough, as did some others who had burdened themselves with more possessions than they could carry swiftly, yet strangely refused to let go. It was not yet noon.

The earth was wet and slippery underfoot as Little Turtle and most of the others turned back from the pursuit of the fleeing troops. Looking up, the Miami chief felt an elation akin to the clear skies and the sun high overhead. The Indians had erased the invading army as surely as the sun had burned off the early morning snow.

But if the skies and the forests were alive in the cool November sunlight, there were reminders of death all along the route north towards the battle scene. Bodies of soldiers, usually stripped and scalped, marked the way. Mostly, they had been the wounded, unable to keep up with the running pace. A few dead Indians were also found. They, having grown careless, had learned too late that even a vanquished wasp can sting.

While passing a ditch, the Turtle came across a young red-headed militiaman -- one of the mounted Kentucky riflemen who had accompanied the army of St. Clair on what they had expected to be a punishment of the hated Indians and revenge on the villages of the savages. The man, unable to move because of a deep wound to the abdomen, was still conscious.

Little Turtle began to question him concerning the numbers of men with St. Clair at the encampment, and what troops the Americans might have available from the forts further to the south.

The wounded soldier, eyes wide with fear, said the army had between 1,500 and 1,600 men at the start of the attack by the Indians that morning along the Wabash stream. He also told the Miami chief he believed there were about 600 additional soldiers at the several stockades from Fort Jefferson to Fort Washington on the Ohio. Later when Little Turtle was taking a body count, he would find that half of the entire American army had been killed at the battle site and along the route of retreat south.

The war chief looked down at the militiaman. He knew the information the young man gave him was substantially correct, confirming both reports by scouts and his own observations. As he looked, the Turtle wondered rather irrelevantly why the youth had not cut off the scraggly beginnings of a beard. He decided to show compassion. "Kill him quickly," he said to The Snake.

Continuing back to the battle site, Little Turtle first saw hundreds of vultures which had started their impatient circles overhead. The scene itself, despite the general desolation of bodies and material, was peculiarly businesslike.

In the few hours since the attack and retreat, marauding Indians had removed everything of value or use, or which might be colorful or token. Bodies still lay where they fell. Only a few of the wounded were unfortunate enough to be still alive.

Near the center of the compound, the Turtle noticed a large hole in the ground was engaging the attention and energy of busily digging Indians. Sitting to one side was Le Gris, now sightless and one arm in a sling of bloody buff and blue cloth. His one eye had swollen closed following a heavy blow to the side of the head during the attack on the artillery position.

After his struggle with General Butler and taking temporary refuge in an army tent, Le Gris was again trampled to the ground when charging horses crashed into the thing. While lying there, he found with his hands that a large digging operation had recently taken place. The old Miami chief surmised something had been buried.

Four feet into the earth, one of the warriors struck the corner of a box. After being pulled to the surface, it was found to contain three leather bags. The Indian quickly thrust his hand into one of them, and clutched in his fingers gold coins, which he held up for all to see.

St. Clair had been carrying $38,000 in gold on the expedition in the expectation of supplying permanent outposts at three rivers near Miamitown and at other key places along the Maumee. When defeat became obvious, the general had told Lt. Col. William Darke, who covered the retreating army, to bury the gold.

Little Turtle said, "Let each brave of the many tribes here share in these coins."

He then turned and looked across the entire clearing. "We will take no prisoners from this place. Leave all of the dead where they lie. Of the enemy, fill every mouth with clay, so all those who come later to these grounds will see that the land of the Indians cannot be taken cheaply."

Chapter 8

Colonel John Hardin's luck ran out on April Fools' Day, 1792, along the banks of the Maumee.

Hardin, one of the most persistent and dashing of the Indian fighters, was known throughout the Old Northwest as a leader of the Kentucky mounted riflemen. He rode with General Josiah Harmar in the ill-fated attack on Miamitown in 1790 and the disaster of General Arthur St. Clair the following year. He went on numerous other raids and rescues in Kentucky and along the Ohio. He survived them all.

Now, however, the Kentucky colonel was sent on a mission of peace. He and Major Alexander Trueman, a federal officer, were on their way to Miamitown to feel out the Indian chiefs on possible treaty terms. Their trip was the opening round of an effort by the Washington Administration to gain on the peace table what the military had failed to get on the field of battle.

The two emissaries never made it to their destination. Hardin, Trueman and several others with them were killed by Indians, probably Shawnee, as they were traveling up the Maumee.

When Little Turtle heard about the slaying of the American representatives, he was indifferent. For one thing, he usually chose to never speak with agents and envoys of the enemy. He spoke only French and the Indian dialects. He often did not trust the interpreters who came along with the emissaries, or even the white Indian partisans, such as Alexander McKee and Simon Girty, to give honest readings and interpretations.

The Miami chief also knew from experience that envoys of the Americans only came to get something -- never to concede to the Indian terms or bind themselves to permanent agreements. But mostly, Little Turtle feared the emissaries of peace more than he feared the invading soldiers. They were a source of divisiveness upon the

Indian lands. They attempted to buy off individual tribes with preferred treatment, or, they would exact terms from some weak-kneed or ignorant village chief, then say the terms applied over a wide area.

Little Turtle returned to the Shawnees the scalps of the envoys and told them to bury the bodies in an unmarked place. This was not the sort of thing to pass on to the British. He did, however, reward the warriors with gifts of new English long-barrel rifles.

To discourage more delegations from coming into the Indian territory, the Turtle sent a message to Washington, the first of many communications between the chief of the Miamis and three Presidents of the United States. The first note, however, was not of a friendly nature.

Little Turtle reminded President Washington of the recent and great victories of the Miami Confederacy over the Federal army. He said the Ohio River would remain as the Indians' border between their own lands and those of the Thirteen States. He also said: "You sent us at different times different speeches, and the bearers thereof our foolish young men killed on their way." He didn't mention any regrets.

Little Turtle at this time was riding high. He was acclaimed and hero worshipped wherever he went -- the Indian towns, the trade centers and the military and government posts as far as Quebec.

But the seeds of eventual defeat were already springing roots -- far away in Paris where the French Revolution was entering its terrorist and ultra-nationalistic phase. Secret diplomacy stemming from a gathering European war was to undo the Indians later at the key moment in their fight to preserve themselves from the Americans.

In the meantime, it was a hot dusty day in August, 1792, when Little Turtle threw down a knife at the feet of three Huron (Wyandot) chiefs. The Indians of the confederacy were in grand council at the Auglaise, a spot where downtown Defiance, Ohio, is located today. The Wyandots, influenced by the Iroquois Chief Brant, talked of concessions to the Americans along the Ohio River area.

"If the Wyandot squaws want to lie on their backs at the Ohio, let them cross knives with us here today," the Turtle

66

said in slow even tones. The Wyandot chiefs looked cautiously around the council fire. They then sat down.

The following year, American Secretary of State Henry Knox sent three peace commissioners to the British garrison at Fort Niagara to seek a treaty with the Indians. They were Benjamin Lincoln, Timothy Pickering and Beverly Randolph. They were to meet with the new British governor of Upper Canada, John Graves Simcoe. Simcoe soon learned that President Washington had given the commissioners private instructions to concede everything to the Indians, except for two small settlement areas along the Ohio River. One of these was at Cincinnati and the other at Marietta. After the disaster of the St. Clair campaign, the government appeared to be relaxing its claims to the Old Northwest for the first time since the Act of 1783.

The Indians, however, were not in a receptive frame of mind. Beside, they would have had a difficult time distinguishing an honest move to negotiate after the wearing series of phony ones.

Little Turtle watched as Cat's Eyes of the Shawnees, Sawaghdawunk of the Wyandots and Simon Girty walked down towards the river's edge to a canoe.

The warchief and ancient Le Gris had handpicked the threesome deliberately as an insult to the high-ranking American delegation which had arrived at Detroit to continue peace conferences with the British and the Indians. Behind the Turtle's action was a very basic ambition -- to keep the Indian confederacy intact and secure his own position at his head.

Both Le Gris and Little Turtle were laughing over glasses of Spanish wine (even the Spaniards on the Lower Mississippi were now backing the Turtle's army). The two chiefs went over the names of the three messengers they had just seen off to the big meeting along the Detroit River.

First, there was Cat's Eyes, who was tapped for the job by Le Gris. The Shawnee was notorious in both Virginia and Pennsylvania as a horse thief. It was estimated that he stole more than a thousand horses over a 15-year period. He also was quite unsightly because of a skin disease and was for this reason one of the few bearded Indians in the entire territory. Further, he was toothless and in the advanced stages of consumption.

Sawaghdawunk was picked by Little Turtle for more subtle reasons. The Wyandot was an especially virile-looking warrior who had some years earlier violated the sister of Brant, the Iroquois chief. The Turtle, who detested Brant, correctly surmised the Iroquois would surface at the conference and start making his usual speeches.

As for the brutish American turncoat Simon Girty, his very name was a curse on the frontier and beyond. He had lived at various Indian villages for years. Though he joined the Americans briefly during the Revolution, he soon ducked out and later was leading the Indians in savage raids on American settlements.

This selected trio was on its way to meet with President Washington's commissioners: Lincoln of Massachusetts, Pickering of Pennsylvania and Randolph of Virginia. Also participating were John Graves Simcoe, governor of Upper Canada (Canada was divided into two parts, Upper and Lower Canada, in 1791); Col. Richard G. England, British commandant at Detroit, and assistant and observers of all three parties.

"Say only that we are united and will hold all lands north of the Ohio River. Those are the only terms by which both parties can live in peace," Little Turtle told the three men before they departed from the Maumee Rapids. "Remind the representatives of the Thirteen States that the chief of the Miamis cannot trust to any of their agreements so long as their new army continues to build strongholds on Indian land along the lower Miami."

Little Turtle was referring to the growing army of General Anthony Wayne, which by this time had rebuilt two forts north from Cincinnati, and was preparing to raise another at Greeneville, a strong point still further north.

Later, when Little Turtle was told the American commissioners would agree to the Ohio River boundary, except for the towns of Cincinnati and Marietta along the Ohio, and that money would be paid to the Indians for those two sites, the Miami warchief said: "Let them take the money and give it to the white squatters, so they can remove themselves from the lands of our fathers."

In the privacy of the cabin along the Maumee, near where the chiefs of the many tribes had been in council at the Rapids, the Turtle told Le Gris of his discontent. The new British administration in the western lakes area was quite another thing from times past. Simcoe, the governor of Upper Canada, was anxious for a decision over the Americans to enhance his reputation with the Home Office. There was little real understanding, however, of either uniting the Indians and preparing them for large-scale warfare, or what the long-term results might be. England, who had replaced de Peyster as Detroit commandant, had little of the anti-American tenacity of the former Tory.

"All the Indians of the many nations can be pleased with the terms which our victories have brought from the American capital," the Turtle later said to the assembled chiefs, "but we will not concede any of our lands, and we cannot come to terms with them so long as there is a knife to our backs." The fires along the Maumee burned long into the night. Before dawn, Little Turtle left the circle to prepare for a long journey. He sensed that something was amiss; and something he didn't know about.

With the earthen breastworks of the old French fort to his back, Little Turtle looked west across the Plains of Abraham.

The Miami chief was mostly content with his trip to Quebec; and his visit to the famous battleground added to his mood.

"General Wolfe died near this very spot," said Lord Dorchester. "He probably never knew of the great victory; nor did Montcalm, the French commander who was also killed in the battle."

The Turtle smiled and turned toward the English governor-general of Canada. "If it had turned out differently, neither of us would be standing here today. As for the generals, perhaps they have the fortune who die in the time of their glory."

As they walked back to the Chateau St. Louis, high above the St. Lawrence River where the Chateau Frontenac is located today, Little Turtle spoke with a rather blunt bland confidence. "Nothing will serve our purpose so well as a fort at the river by the lake. It will show the many tribes we can depend on our friends from across the great sea. It will help keep rifles and powder in the hands of our braves."

"You put me in a difficult position," said Lord Dorchester. "Of course we desire to help our Indian friends in every reasonable manner. But as you know, the Foreign Office in London is most anxious to avoid any open incident at this time which might draw the Thirteen States into the hostilities on the side of France. We must be circumspect."

After a moment, Little Turtle said, "We will all be undone if the confederacy of the many tribes is broken. I can hold here in my hand the warriors of the rivers and the lakes, but more is needed if we are to have the nations from the north and the east. I must be able to show them something now. Later, if we have destroyed the new American army, no one will question your policies of success."

That night, Little Turtle and his sister's son, Jean Baptiste de Richardville, joined Lord Dorchester (Guy Carleton) and John Graves Simcoe, governor of Upper Canada, in an ornate chamber of the old fortress. Chateau St. Louis had been the seat of government almost since the founding of Quebec. Also at the winter meeting of early 1794 were several other Indian chiefs and British military commanders.

British interests at the time were double-edged. The Crown wanted to maintain its political hand and trading concession profits in the Great Lakes area, but also wanted to avoid a breach with the Americans which might make them allies of the French in a war which had begun the previous year.

Lord Dorchester decided on a course which was quite

different from that which it appeared to be. He ordered Simcoe to build a stockade, to be called Fort Miami and just up-river from present-day Toledo. This would show the Indians that the British were supporting Little Turtle and the fight of the tribes against the Americans.

Also at the Feb. 10 meeting, Lord Dorchester told the Indian chiefs: "I shall not be surprised if we are at war with them (The United States) in the course of the present year. We have borne the language and conduct of the people of the U. S. with patience, but I believe our patience is almost exhausted."

The statement produced much excitement among the various Indian chiefs, and the word spread quickly through the territory. The Americans eventually got wind of the Dorchester statement to the Indians, possibly through some inside tip by a British underling who hoped to embarrass the governor-general. The Washington Administration registered a loud protest to the British Foreign Office. The London government replied that the whole thing was a fabrication.

Privately, Lord Dorchester told Little Turtle the American army must never be permitted to approach the British fort near the mouth of the Maumee, since this would risk an open breach and possible military confrontation between the two countries. The presence of such a fort on lands previously ceded by the British to the United States was a clear violation of the treaty at the conclusion of the Revolutionary War. Any approaching American armies must be defeated earlier in the wilderness.

It was an era of two-faced diplomacy -- like most any other.

Little Turtle was the sort of burden the new Republic of the United States simply wasn't expecting.

Annoyance, and then anger, gave way to frustration and finally disillusionment. The annoyance came with the Indian resistance to the settling of the lands along the Ohio River. Anger was experienced with the defeat of General Harmar and the other expedition leaders. Finally, frustration and bloody disillusionment set in with the decimation of the army of General Arthur St. Clair, who doubled as governor of the Northwest Territory.

These unexpected setbacks, and an attempt to soften them, can be seen in a message to the joint Senate and House of Representatives on Dec. 12, 1791, delivered by President Washington.

"It is with great concern that I communicate to you the information received from Major General St. Clair of the misfortune which has befallen the troops under his command.

"Although the national loss is considerable according to the scale of the event, yet it may be repaired without great difficulty, excepting as to the brave men who have fallen on the occasion, and who are subject of public as well as private regret."

The following year, Washington sent another message to Congress in which he requested a large appropriation for the conscription and supplying of a new army. He mentioned "new and outrageous proofs of persevering hostility on the part of the tribes with whom we are in contest." At this time, Anthony Wayne was named commander of the army of the United States.

It must have seemed inconceivable to the leaders of the young republic, fresh from a victorious war with the world's greatest power, that a lone native of the wilderness could keep a ragtag assemblage of Indians in the field year after year, cutting down and decimating every organized military force the government could field.

The Turtle was a man of resourcefulness and quiet thoroughness. He seems to have been the only Indian leader who grasped at once the complexities of international politics and their bearing on the Indians' defense, and the need of the Indians for consistent support of an industrial nation's war material. Added to this was his tactical superiority over every general who opposed him, and his ability to keep in line the naive and undisciplined tribesmen of the forests.

Yet, events were to undo Little Turtle and his Indian army at the crucial moment. And the Miami warchief himself was one of the first to see the developing circumstances.

Some have said Little Turtle and his confederacy overplayed their hand, when, after they defeated St. Clair's army, they turned aside the Americans' offer to leave the Indians all the lands north of the Ohio River except for two settlements along the waterway.

But Little Turtle mistrusted the treaty proposition because the army of Anthony Wayne was already poised north of Cincinnati. If he had had to come to terms as some of the British had advised, the Indian tribes would have dispersed and divided, thus placing the entire Indian lands at the mercy of the American army which should chose to violate the treaty terms and invade. The Turtle did not place a high value on treaties. He knew they were only of use so long as there was the power to back them up.

Through the cold early months of 1794, the growing army of the United States could be seen drilling and moving about the newly-constructed fort at Greeneville, Ohio. The spies of the Turtle, ducking along the snow trails of the forest, had to be more alert than on earlier campaigns with the American troops. Wayne had brought with him numerous Choctaw and Cherokee scouts, both ancestorial enemies of the Miamis. On occasion, they would grab a careless brave, drag him back to the confines of the fort, and by the most painful techniques imaginable, extract information concerning the whereabouts of Little Turtle's warriors. This method served Wayne through the entire campaign, protecting the American army from large-scale surprises.

The images of starvation were often in the eyes of Little Turtle during the early summer of 1794. The villages were crowded with squaws and children from a dozen Indian tribes, some from hundreds of miles away. The warriors were finding game thin and sparse in the usually abundant forests. It was the wrong season and too many hunters had been too long flushing the game.

The Miamis and their confederate tribes had been in almost constant contact with the army of General Anthony Wayne for nearly a year. Increasingly, the Indians came

73

to depend on the American supply trains for provisions. Each raid on the horse and mule trains took on more of an aspect of daring stabs at putting food on the table.

A year or two earlier it had been different. At that time Little Turtle had caught several large supply movements between Cincinnati and the several forts that were being erected to the north. One such raid, against a group headed by Major John Adair, was a battle in itself, involving about 100 soldiers and nearly twice that number of Indians. The warriors captured most of the horses and supplies and killed six soldiers. The Indian losses were about the same.

But by June of the year of the major campaign, the pickings were getting thin. In a rather ironic aside to Chief Pacan, the old Miami negotiator, the Turtle said, "Our trouble is that we have an overabundancc of braves and squaws."

Little Turtle had in mind the more than 2,000 warriors from the many tribes who had come months before from as far as the Mississippi country and the land of the northern Great Lakes. In many instances, entire families migrated to the Miami villages in the area of the Maumee.

"It is not the way of our people for a brave to leave behind his family for many moons when he goes afar, and even suspects he may never return. The soldiers of the Black Snake (the Turtle's name for Anthony Wayne) have this advantage over us. They need only look after themselves."

Pacan agreed with the Turtle about the desperate condition of many of the thousands of Indian peoples scattered throughout the vicinity. "We will find it difficult to hold together much longer, but the Americans are having their troubles also. Again today our young men came across the grave of one of the soldiers, shot many times in the chest."

The old chief was referring to the body of an arrant soldier who had been retaken by the Americans and shot for desertion. The daily log of General Wayne attests to the accuracy of Pacan's observation. Hardly is there a date for which there is not an entry about breaches of discipline and the laying on of lashings. Occasionally, there would be the listing of the name of a runaway executed for desertion. Wayne for two years had been using every possible means to avoid the carelessness which might have been a factor in the massacre of so many of Harmar's and St. Clair's men.

The Indians had watched hungrily the previous winter as troops under Wayne erected Fort Recovery and on the very site of the defeat of General St. Clair's army two and a half years before. They had not attacked at that time because Little Turtle was far away in Canada, and also, the plan had been to draw General Wayne's troops far enough to completely isolate them from the regular supply.

When arriving at the scene of the battle along the upper Wabash stream, the Americans gasped. More than 600 skulls, many still clayfilled, were lying on the ground surface. Bone figures in contorted shapes, some staked down, gave sickening suggestions of things that had transpired there. Skeletons and near skeletons of women were marked by short spears which protruded up from the middle of their bodies. The carnage and suffering was now terribly mute, and was more chilling than the deep frost.

With the passing of the months and completion of the fort, the pressure for action went over to the Indians. "Let us speak with Le Gris and Blue Jacket," the Turtle said to Pacan. "We will meet where the oaks grow tall along the stream of the Shawnees. I plan to post braves in the light and in the darkness near their brash building (newly-built Fort Recovery). Our people cannot wait while the enemy continues their long rest, or until the snow flies. We will all be bones by that day."

Chapter 9

Anthony Wayne was born on New Year's Day, 1745, about seven years before the birth of Little Turtle.

Of all the generals of the American Revolution, Wayne was probably the most universally acclaimed at the end of the war. He led troops in every theatre -- New York, New Jersey, Pennsylvania, Virginia, the Carolinas and Georgia.

It was during his sudden storming of Stony Point in 1779 that the nickname "Mad" was added to Anthony. It was originally coined by a deserter, who when taken into custody, complained of serving with "that madman." Wayne was the General Patton of the Revolution. His associates as well as the enemy were often caught off balance by his quick strokes and surprising changes in tactics.

Wayne made decisive moves again and again. He quickly grabbed West Point after Benedict Arnold defected; led the Americans at Brandywine and Monmouth; and took on the larger army of Cornwallis at Green Springs, Va., then as quickly extricated his army with small loses.

He was 37 years old when the hostilities ended, and like some others who are spectacular in war, he never quite made it in time of peace. Following the election of 1790, he was deprived of a seat in Congress because of alleged vote frauds in Georgia.

It was more than a year and a half later that President Washington named Wayne as commander of the U. S. Army. The troops had been badly mauled at the hands of the Indians of the Miami Confederacy, and the military was demoralized by public apathy. It had been 10 years since Wayne had last served in a war campaign. He was 47 years old by this time. His job was to put together a new army and do battle with a military leader, younger than himself, who had been in the field of battle consistently for the past 15 years.

Little Turtle first heard of General Mad Anthony Wayne from the British informants following Wayne's appointment in 1792. There was no question in the Miami warchief's mind as to the reason for the appointment or the aims of the new American commander.

"Our friends at Detroit tell us the American Congress is giving big money for a new army to come against us," the Turtle said at the time. "We shall watch every river and count every man. We will await the sunrise of each day, and when they have come far enough, the sons of all the Indian nations will be ready."

As the braves of Little Turtle watched, they found that Wayne was slow in the coming. The Miami chieftain, informed of Wayne's reputation for sudden strokes during the Revolution, was prepared for quick, harsh, decisive battles. But Wayne, after moving down the Ohio River from Pittsburgh to Cincinnati, hardly made a move for a year. And then only to erect better forts a short distance to the north.

"Either the American general is attempting to deceive us, or he is waging war like an old woman," Le Gris said to the Turtle. The chiefs were sitting in a smoky log building located along Spy Run Creek, a short distance north of the St. Mary's River at Miamitown. The Turtle displayed a little unusual bad temper, possibly due to a combination of the sleet and freezing rain and the fact that a few recent raids along the Ohio had gone astray. In one of these attacks on the river traffic, The Snake had been killed. The Turtle particularly prized the slippery Shawnee chief for his constant harassment of American supply trains and his ability to snatch stragglers -- always a good source of information.

On his last day, The Snake had attempted to stop a convoy of supply rafts coming down the Ohio. First, he attempted a ruse which was designed to play on the Americans' sympathy. In this, he forced a woman captive to shout for help from the north bank of the waterway. The group on the raft didn't bite. Possibly they were sympathetic, but the trick had been used before.

The Snake then had his party hurry further down stream. Several of the braves crossed to the south side. Then they waited until the rafts floated that far. As the convoy approached, the Indians on the south side of the Ohio began to fire their flintlocks -- the aim being to drive the rafts toward the north bank where The Snake and most of his raiders were concealed. This didn't work either. The current was so fast the rafts continued down the main stream in spite of efforts of some of the boatmen to do just what the Indians wanted them to.

With this, The Snake and some of his party took to the river in canoes. Paddling frantically, they began to close the distance, but were met with a stream of rifle shot. Several warriors were hit but they pressed on. Catching up to the rear-most rafts, the Indians boarded in a struggle of hammers and axes.

According to the story later received by Little Turtle, The Snake was cut in the stomach and pushed overboard by a burly woman, the wife of a German brewer. He was last seen going into the icy water and being carried away in the river current.

The Turtle's unease was not helped by these events or the difficult supply situation of his own. He had too many warriors at hand too soon. He did not expect General Wayne to bring his army up the same trails as Generals Harmar and St. Clair before him.

Almost daily, the Miami chief expected some trick -- a sudden dash of American troops toward the Wabash or to the Indian rear across the lakes. But no, Wayne came up the identical old route; and then, instead of the anticipated march toward Miamitown, the American general settled down at Fort Greeneville for the entire winter.

With a look of disgust on his lined and scarred face, Chief Le Gris again spoke across the rough walnut table. "I don't think that old squaw is ever going to come out of his hut."

"Maybe the Black Snake is like the fox in his hole," replied the Turtle. "He is not asleep. He has one eye open for any chickens which come by his place."

The Indian chiefs remained in the log shelter, protecting

78

themselves from the bitter February weather and discussing the apparent non-action of Mad Anthony Wayne. The American general, called the Black Snake by Little Turtle, was keeping his army under cover at Greeneville for the entire winter of 1793-94.

"We must watch while he waits; then we must wait a little longer," the Turtle said quietly. He looked out the door, rather absent-mindedly studying the sleet and freezing rain. Turning back into the room, he told the several Shawnee and Miami chiefs: "I want him far into our country so others cannot come to help him."

The Turtle knew some of the chiefs were impatient with the long months of relative inaction. As before, he mitigated their discontent. "I would move now over the frozen rivers and swamps, but he will not. He does not have an Indian army. He must use horses. And the horses must have the green grasses of spring."

The Miami warchief was more worried at that moment about the lack of snow -- needed by hunting parties to follow the tracks of games in the forests. It had been a strange winter, and disappointing in many respects. Bitter cold and high winds were followed by freezing rains and hard sleet. This was not the sort of weather to feed the thousands of tribesmen and their families who were in the vicinity of Miamitown. Even the deer and raccoon of the wilderness, like the soldiers of Fort Greeneville, had disappeared. Only the wolves could be seen trotting and sniffing across the frozen landscape.

On the following morning, Little Turtle and his hunting party departed from Kekionga and headed west. They stopped momentarily, however, to gaze at the frozen bodies of two Choctaw Indians which hung from a pair of oak trees beside the small stream.

Tecumseh had brought the Choctaw spies to Miamitown two weeks before. Spies for Wayne's army, the Choctaws were nabbed by the Shawnees as the two were picking their way along the Maumee River near the present location of Antwerp, Ohio.

The pair of Choctaws were in such poor condition by the

time the Turtle could question them, they could give little information of value to the Miami warchief. He told Le Gris and Tecumseh to get rid of them. Thus the Choctaw pair ended up being hung between the two old oaks, and giving a name to Spy Run Creek which has lasted to this day.

The hunting party continued west, across a frozen swamp to the high ground of an Indian trail leading to Eel River. The snow was falling in blinding billows as the Indians came into the village of Little Turtle, some miles west of the present Churubusco.

The Turtle had learned a few days before of the death of his Mohican mother. She had died in the smallpox epidemic which was sweeping the Indian villages that winter.

Standing with the Turtle in the snow as the body was being prepared for burial was his sister, Tacumwa. She was the wife of a French trader, Joseph Drouet de Richardville. In her early years, Tacumwa was known from the Great Lakes to the Mississippi as a girl of striking beauty. Like her brother, the Turtle, she had had at least some schooling in the Canadian settlements of the French during her childhood.

Now in middle age, she was still a handsome woman, and a very energetic one. Her husband, who claimed a relationship with the Bourbon family (distant cousin Louis XVI was guillotined the year before in Paris), was now living in Canada. Tacumwa, or Madame de Richardville, did not miss her heavy-drinking husband. She operated a fur-trading business which extended from Detroit to Vincennes, and reportedly maintained several diverting social connections.

As they stood in the snow alone on the hill near Devil's Lake, the Turtle said to her, "I would rather we did not leave her in a sitting grave, above the ground. Let us return in the spring and bury her in the way of our father's tribe." Tacumwa looked at Little Turtle and nodded. But neither of them returned the following spring.

Events moved quickly with the thaw and rush of river

80

waters in 1794. Little Turtle and his raiding party were hurrying south along the Great Miami River to intercept a heavily armed supply train which was moving from Fort Washington on the Ohio to Fort Greeneville, where General Wayne was assembling additional troops for his major push.

The Turtle had hoped to catch the Americans as they were taking 700 packhorses across the swollen river. Failing that, he attacked the convoy on high ground, 18 miles north of Cincinnati. The Miami warchief had had at least some success in cutting off the supplies for Wayne's army. Some deserters were complaining of starving. However, the many Indians of the Miami Confederation were also in bad shape, probably in more serious want of provisions than the Americans.

But Little Turtle had one further aim in mind -- the capture of Captain William Clark. Clark, who later would become famous for his trip to the Pacific with Meriwether Lewis, was the younger brother of George Roger Clark, one of the American raiders who specialized in decimating Indian villages -- men, women and children going in one burning sweep.

It was not Little Turtle's Day. The Miami chief and the 40 warriors with him succeeded in cutting the convoy in two parts, but couldn't hold the train. Captain Clark with 20 dragoons and about 65 infantrymen swung around to the the rear of the Indians. The Turtle's raiders had to run for the protection of a swamp and heavy brush. In the meantime, the supply train escaped.

"With the flow of our cousins, the Ottawas and Chippewas, and the many nations, we will have to depart from game which I would have preferred," Little Turtle told Blue Jacket, the Shawnee chief. It was a few weeks later and the Miami warchief was considering the many warriors of the northern tribes who had joined the Indian forces.

Blue Jacket grinned back at the Turtle. He had never been in favor of the Miami chieftain's tactics of outwaiting and cutting off the troops of the Americans. He also was prone to using the term "squaws war" to describe the more subtle strategy. "The Shawnee goes straight at the enemy, knowing in his heart the bravest warriors will strike the more deadly blow."

It was an indirect jab at the Turtle, whom he served out of fear and necessity more than respect. Fear because most of his braves would go over to the Miami chief if he balked and because his own life would be in jeopardy at the hands of Le Gris and his strange allies, the Kickapoo and Mingo. Necessity because the Turtle had been able for many years to maintain a relationship of trust and confidence with the British sources of war supplies.

But now, the Turtle decided the Indians needed decisive action. There were more than 2,000 braves in the field, many of them hungry and impatient.

It is ironic that the battle which ensued is one of the few in which the Indians under the Turtle far outnumbered the Americans, yet turned out to be their most costly defeat. In fact, though largely ignored by historians, and not realized by the Indians themselves at the time, the battle for Fort Recovery turned out to be the key test of the whole war.

Little Turtle carefully calculated the chances of storming the newly-built fort on the upper stream of the Wabash. The stockade had been erected a few months before on the very site where the warriors of the Miami chief had destroyed the army of General Arthur St. Clair three years earlier.

"We will see if the Black Snake has taught his soldiers any new tricks," the Turtle said to Pacan, the Miami chief, and Little Otter, chief of the Ottawa. "Let us surround them in the night, and just as the sun first puts them at rest and tempts their hunger, our braves will be like flies on their timber."

The Turtle knew there were about 200 riflemen inside of Fort Recovery. Surprise and timing would be needed to overcome such a number in a protected stockade stance. Both of these qualities were destroyed by something which in other circumstances would have seemed like a lucky stroke.

Just as the Indians were silently moving up over the

damp June grass, the gates of the fort opened and out flowed a huge train of pack animals, driven by a 140-man brigade of riflemen and horsemen who had arrived the previous day from Fort Greeneville.

Little Turtle had a feeling for the land and the life that was in it. In the hours before dawn, he was thinking of the first honey bee of the day, which could be expected to emerge just as the first rays of sun gave warmth to the hive. He was amused by the thought of the bees, and most animal life in natural surroundings, carefully seeking the safety of hives or precise shelters during the night hours.

This was not the case with the Indians, nor the wolves or lynx. They were at odds with the rest of nature. They sought the special advantages the darkness bestows on the few. But, thought Little Turtle, even the wolf and cat disappear in that last hour before the new day.

Men too have difficulty in resisting sleep just before dawn. And, he had noticed, the first moments of daylight have a special weight about them for those who have seen the night through, such as those sentries on the walls of Fort Recovery across the way.

The Miami warchief was thinking along these lines when he was alerted by the snap of a twig. In the dim light he could see by the shuffling gait that it was Le Gris, the old chief of the Kekionga Miamis, who was coming near.

"They do not move," said Le Gris. "Maybe 300 horses and more than 100 soldiers. They all stay near the walls of the fort."

"One does not swat the mosquito without awakening the dog," said the Turtle. He was annoyed that the supply train did not move off from the stockade. He assessed again the position of the more than 2,000 warriors who were poised in the scrub and trees. Surprise had been his design for that predawn of June 30, 1794. But storming the walls of Fort Recovery in a surprise stroke was not possible on that morning.

"Come with me. There is the chance these bugs can be turned to fish bait," said the Miami warchief.

Little Turtle stepped carefully along the bank of the small stream of the upper Wabash, in what is now western Ohio. Near the fort he motioned to Captain Johnny, the

Shawnee chief, to send braves in an immediate attack on the convoy.

The Turtle, together with Le Gris, Tecumseh, Blue Jacket and most of the other Indians stayed hidden in the brush. The first glimmers of the new day were giving bland shadowless light as the warriors under Captain Johnny went screaming at the supply train escort.

The entire convoy jumped to life like startled swine. Gun shots mingled with shouts and curses. Horses lifted and strained in harnesses, adding to the general shrill dim.

As Little Turtle watched, he could see the Indians were rapidly in and through the horses, going after the soldiers of the escort. There appeared to be more men than originally supposed, possibly 150, the Turtle thought.

The soldiers, however, did not hold their ground, which Little Turtle had hoped would draw some of the 200 men in the garrison out of the stockade to rescue the men and horse of the supply train.

Instead, most of the Americans of the escort group made a dash for the fort. Some ran on foot. Others made sudden turns on horses and went for the stockade gates. A few bravely stood and contested with the Indians.

Only several minutes had passed. But it served to alert the entire garrison. As Little Turtle and the massed army of the Indians rose up from the shadows and rushed at the stockade walls, a withering wave of rifle and cannon fire met them.

Many of the warriors reached the upright timbers of the fort, but few managed to reach the top and even fewer went over the palisade. These later few were either shot at point blank or were pushed back to the ground. After several futile efforts at forcing open the gates, the Miami chief waved for the warriors to retire to the cover of the forest.

The battle settled down to sporadic rifle fire between the soldiers in Fort Recovery and the Indians in the surrounding woods. The braves were to make several more rushes at the stockade during a long hot day and after darkness.

In the meantime, the sweetish odor of burning horse flesh came to the Turtle's nostrils. Looking further back in the bush, he could see great fires which had been built. Some of the 220 horses taken in the raid were already hanging from huge spits over the flames.

Indians were no more fond of horse meat than anyone else. But much of the Indian army had been near starvation for several weeks. If there was a feast, it was not an especially palatable one. To Little Turtle, neither was the Battle of Fort Recovery.

The Miami warchief listened carefully to each shot from the stockade. He was trying to determine the ammunition situation of the Americans. If the shots came only occasionally when there was an obvious and inviting target, then that would mean they were counting each ball and were fearful of running out. But he could detect nothing of the sort. Rather, the soldiers were firing more freely than usual, it seemed.

Light from torches reflected crazily across the clearing as the Indians rushed toward the stockade and heaved the flames over the timbers. Little Turtle stood nearby in the shadows of the trees, his eyes scanning the fort to see if any of the fires caught hold, possibly giving an opening to the Indians for the sacking of the redoubt. Nothing of substance was gained.

The night continued and occasional rifle fire could be heard as the time passed in rather desolutory fashion. In the meantime, the Indians were dragging away the dead and wounded.

For a full day and most of the night, the assault of the fort had been without advantage to the Indians. Even the midnight burning of one of the soldiers, captured the previous morning during the raid on the supply train failed in its purpose. The man, a federal regular from Richmond, Va., was strapped to a dry-stick-and-straw rack and pushed near the fort's gates. No sooner had the rack been ignited, however, when two shots rang out from the stockade, putting the captive out of his misery.

With the coming of morning, the smell of animal fat from the torches was still heavy in the soft mist along the river edge. The Turtle had by this time decided the further assault of the fort was useless and costly. Losses up to this point had not been great, considering the numbers of

Indians engaged. But it was the time to withdraw. Among other things, the ammunition of the Indians was nearly depleted.

The Miami warchief counted forty-six warriors dead out of the more than 2,000 Indians at the scene. As far as he could tell, there were twenty-one Americans killed, and possibly more inside the fort.

Little Turtle was not one to conserve ammunition. He did not believe as most military leaders on the frontier in making every shot count, and holding powder and lead for another day. It was the Turtle's view that battles are won or lost in the first few minutes. His braves therefore poured thousands of rounds of lead into an assault in what might appear to be reckless abandon. On most occasions, the Miami chieftain's tactics had swept him to shocking victories over his enemies. Fort Recovery, however, was an exception.

As the Turtle watched the clear water ripple past his foot dangling in the stream, he knew he had a problem. In withdrawing, the warriors of the many nations were sure to feel a sense of frustration and defeat. Many would now want to return to their native villages, some of which were far away to the north of the Great Lakes. He decided on a strategem to keep an Indian army in the field.

"Draw off your braves and tell them we shall have council where the Auglaise flows into our river," the Turtle told several of the chiefs. "Your young men must save themselves for the night when the moon crosses over to our backs. In that light we will surprise the intruders when their army is in the forest. Now, I must go to seek from our friends in Detroit those things we will need for our revenge of this night."

A large portion of the Indian confederacy did go to the Maumee River area to await the next stroke in the war against General Anthony Wayne. Some, however, left for lands far away and were never to return. These included the Chippewa from the north, the Fox from the west and part of the Potawatomis from the Lake Michigan area. Staying in the hopes of bushwacking Wayne's expedition were the Miamis, the Mingos, the Shawnees, the Delawares, the Ottawas, the Wyandots and the Kickapoos. For the most part, they had little choice; it was their villages which were being threatened.

Little Turtle, however, did not immediately leave on his mission to the British. He said to Le Gris, "I will seek a talk with the faithful husband of my daughter. I will wait for him to the west, at the place where we have so often assembled by the stream of the water animals (Salamonie River)."

The person mentioned by the Miami warchief for whom he waited fruitlessly for three days was a white man in whom Little Turtle placed unusual trust, considering his usual attitude. His name was William Wells and he was the husband of Sweet Breeze, the Turtle's daughter.

The Miami warchief was still thinking of schemes which might yet bring about the devastation of the invading Americans. Or, failing that, possibly some other advantages. Wells, he considered, might play a subtle yet useful role in either case.

William Wells learned early to look out for himself. He was so good at it, except for one final occasion, that even today his name lives. There is Wells St. in downtown Chicago, Wells County in Indiana, and various avenues and streets in many communities named for Wells, including Fort Wayne and Detroit.

It was always hard to tell where Wells would be when the chips were down. He was fast on his feet in more ways than one. His instincts time and again led him to safe and self-serving havens.

One of the difficulties with Wells was that his associates seldom fared so well. Where Wells was to obtain the choice land at the three rivers post, called Wells Pre-emptive; most of his Indian and white brethren were eventually left in destitution. When Wells was serving in the lucrative position of Indian agent, the welfare of others was in decline. In the long run, however, the Indians were to get to Wells.

At the time of Little Turtle's campaign to choke off the invading forces of Mad Anthony Wayne, Wells was still a young man. It had only been a dozen years since a backwoods boy of 12 years had been grabbed off a farm below the Ohio, which today would be within the city limits of Louisville, Ky. Marauding Miami Indians took the boy across the river and north, where a young Miami warchief took a liking to him.

Little Turtle later adopted Wells and the boy grew into an energetic and handsome man with black curly hair. He became an accepted member of the Indian communities at Miamitown and along the Eel River. In many respects, he imitated the manners and observant habits of Little Turtle. When he was about 20 years old, he married Sweet Breeze, the warchief's delicate and youthful daughter.

Little Turtle was rather enjoying his solitude as he awaited Wells at a grassy opening in the woods near the Salamonie. It had only been a few days since the Indians of the Miami Confederacy were repulsed by the American garrison at Fort Recovery. The colors, the sounds, the smells of life spoke to him, and he was again at home with the earth on which he sat.

Though he was in a hurry to be off to see the British in Canada, he was no longer anxious. He was hopeful, though, that he would soon see Wells guiding his horse along the edge of the stream toward the clearing.

The Turtle carefully went over a web of schemes he had been mentally weaving.

He planned to have Wells tell Wayne he wanted to speak in the tongue of peace. To say the Indian nations have vast numbers of warriors poised in the forests. But to tell him the many chiefs will sit down to council if he can come now to parley with the chief of the Miamis.

He hoped to get from Wells a count of their men, but mostly a count of their horses. That would tell more about when they would move. Then he could count the days, and when the time came, know where to find the enemy.

Little Turtle considered three possible results from a meeting. He did not, however, expect Anthony Wayne to proceed into the wilderness to any immediate meetings.

Quite the opposite, Little Turtle surmised that Wayne would be cautious to act, and would be suspecting some sort of trick. This might delay him, giving Little Turtle time to obtain new arms from the British. Until they had new arms and powder, the Turtle could see no way for the Indians to stop an army the size of Wayne's.

The Turtle also saw the advantage of a potential source of information within the enemy camp. He knew Wells would be closely watched, but he also knew of his son-in-law's skills. In the back of his mind, Little Turtle saw one more, if remote, value. If the Indian confederacy were to be defeated, it might be quite advantageous for him to have a member of his family in the confidence of the victorious forces.

But after three days Wells, who had been serving General Wayne as a spy for nearly two years, did not appear. The Turtle again grew restive. He did not believe Wells would lead an attempt to capture him. But the thought did intrude. The Miami warchief disappeared in a northerly direction.

Little Turtle went to the British fort at Detroit to get rifles and gun powder for his war against the United States.

The Miami Indians wait along the Maumee as American infantrymen come across the river to their deaths in 1790 at the present site of Fort Wayne, Indiana.

Old Le Gris takes a deathgrip on General Richard Butler as the allied Indians under Little Turtle annihilate the U. S. Army under General Arthur St. Clair in 1791 in Western Ohio.

The Shawnee Chief Tecumseh broke with Little Turtle after Anthony Wayne's victory in 1794 and opposed the U. S. until his death in the War of 1812.

The Miami Warchief Little Turtle united the Indian tribes for their greatest victory in American history; but by the time he died years later he was mistrusted and even hated by most of them.

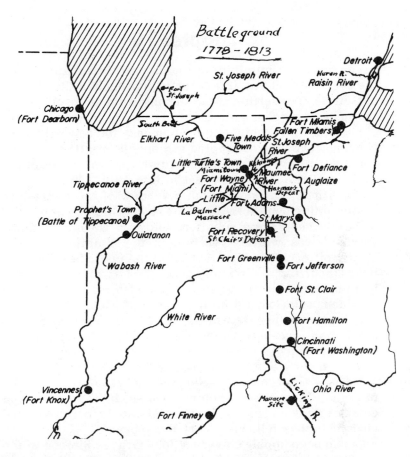

Battleground
1778 - 1813

Detroit

St. Joseph River
Huron R.
Raisin River

Fort St. Joseph

Chicago
(Fort Dearborn)

South Bend

Fort Miamis
Fallen Timbers

Elkhart River

Five Medals
Town

St. Joseph
River

Little Turtle's Town
Miamitown

Fort Defiance

Tippecanoe River

Fort Wayne
(Fort Miami)

Maumee
River

Auglaize

Harmar's
Defeat

Little

Fort Adams

Prophet's Town
(Battle of Tippecanoe)

La Balme
Massacre

St. Marys

Ouiatanon

Fort Recovery
St. Clair's Defeat

Wabash River

Fort Greenville

Fort Jefferson

White River

Fort St. Clair

Fort Hamilton

Cincinnati
(Fort Washington)

Vincennes
(Fort Knox)

Ohio River

Licking R.

Massacre
Site

Fort Finney

The main U. S. Armies came down the Ohio River from
Pittsburgh to Cincinnati and began striking north. These
included forces under General Josiah Harmar in 1790;
General Charles Scott, Col. James Wilkinson and General
Arthur St. Clair in 1791, and General Anthony Wayne in
1794.

Chapter 10

The heat and humidity of the day did not abate during the evening hours as Little Turtle approached the old fort at Detroit. The setting of the sun only added mosquitoes to the general unpleasantness.

The Miami warchief had been uneasy for several days. Now, however, he attempted as hopeful an attitude as he could muster, given the deteriorating circumstances of the Indians of the Old Northwest in late July, 1794.

The Turtle was looking out a window of the fortress to some routine boat activity on the river which flowed down to Lake Erie when a subaltern told him Colonel Richard England was waiting for him in the chambers of the British officer. The Miami warchief had noted earlier that it was the first time in many years the Detroit commander had not met him at the gates. He also missed the easy confident relationship he had had with Colonel Arent de Peyster, an earlier Detroit commander who was a spirited pro-Indian and anti-American partisan through many campaigns.

Colonel England, the bureaucrat, spoke first. "His Majesty's Government welcomes the great chief of the Miamis. I have been hoping to hear further from you concerning your plans, in view of the rather awkward circumstances following Fort Recovery."

"I had been hoping Governor John Graves Simcoe would be present at this council," Little Turtle said. "It is very much on the minds of the many chiefs. We wish to know what assistance we can expect from our brothers here and across the sea. We have great need now for rifles, powder and lead."

"I am sorry to say Governor Simcoe was unable to be here because of other pressing business. If you need signs of our interest in the campaign of your people against the army of General Wayne, you have only to look at the new Fort Miami which we have erected between the rapids of

96

your river and the outflow to Lake Erie.

"As for more guns and ammunition," Colonel England continued, "we are somewhat short at the moment. Perhaps later we can be of more assistance along that line."

The Turtle was deeply astonished, but held himself to an impassive attitude.

"When the colonel says later, can he count the days for his Indian brothers? And when I look to the new fort of your soldiers, can I count the help which is to come from that quarter?"

"Well," the colonel began, "the building of the fort was at the direct orders of Lord Dorchester, not a decision of John Simcoe." He was hinting at the acrid relationship between Lord Dorchester, governor-general of Canada at Quebec, and Simcoe, the lieutenant governor for Upper Canada, which included Ontario and the Detroit area.

"I might as well tell you further," Colonel England said, "that Governor Simcoe has received a note from Lord Dundas, His Majesty's secretary for war. It rather runs counter to the promises Lord Dorchester made to you and the other chiefs last winter.

"The war secretary informs Governor Simcoe that the Jay Treaty is all but successfully completed, assuring peace between the Crown and the Thirteen States. I am afraid this will mean the turning over of all our fortified positions on American Northwest Territories."

The Turtle visibly blanched. "What consideration has been given to the Indian nations in this treaty? What is to be the position of our warriors and our lands. In your dreams, you cannot see our braves throwing stones and spears to stop the American soldiers with their cannon, rifles, and horses."

"I am sorry you do not see the delicacy of my position. The Home Office, as well as the Crown, see the great importance of resolving difficulties and inducing the United States to refrain from engaging in hostilities at this time. We are, you will remember, at war with France."

"We too are at war," said the Miami warchief. "The crow you see there in the sky can fly this very day to where our warriors wait. And not much more to where the

97

enemy, with hard armed men, is poised to sweep us away."

"Perhaps I can make some small provisions in the way of arms here today, but I hope the great chief of the Miamis will understand I can send no new orders across the sea for war supplies at this time."

The Turtle felt a loneliness never previously experienced as he left the post for the suffocating night air along the Detroit River. The political betrayal by the British went to his very bones. In addition, he had just received information that General Wayne had been re-enforced by 1,600 mounted riflemen from Kentucky. Added to the 2,000 federal soldiers already in the field, the American army was now nearly double the dwindling army of the Miami Confederacy.

As Little Turtle stepped into a birch-bark canoe, he said to two confident-looking Miami braves waiting with paddles, "let us go out into the middle of the river and glide with the clear waters as far as the lake. Perhaps the night will be more generous there."

Reflections from the morning sun danced across Lake Erie as far as the shadowy shoreline near the present city of Toledo. The Miami chief leaned over the side of the canoe and drank from the pure blue waters.

Little Turtle could barely make out several figures standing on a sand bar at the mouth of the Maumee River. As the canoe moved closer, he could see the small group of Indians -- both Miami and Shawnee. The Miami, typically, were all but naked and with their long black hair pulled straight back from the face; the Shawnee, wearing buckskin and parts of captured army uniforms, had eagle feathers in headbands.

During the night, the Turtle had looked long at the stars - seeking answers there which he had been unable to find at Detroit. He remembered his own early life and the ways of his people -- so at home with the changing seasons and the sensitive gifts of the wilderness.

That was all threatened now. But hadn't it always been so? The Turtle's earliest memory, no more than an image of a toddler, was of the return of his father one blizzard-like night with the look of near starvation on his face and the brownish gum of dried blood on his cheek and fingers.

His own boyhood had been a short one. And the survival of himself and his village and his people had been his constant occupation ever since. He sometimes saw himself as a tired dog -- always moving but never coming to that place of food and rest. This thought brought before his eyes a campaign many years before.

That first time was so clear he could still feel the breathlessness of it. He had run a half day from the two Iroquois after the scattering of the Miami war party near Niagara. There were times when the two warriors, Senecas he believed, were so close he could smell their sweat. Somehow, he had managed to keep going, just fast enough to put some distance between himself and the pursuers.

That day too, he had come to this same lake -- the far end of it. Trotting down to the sandy shoreline and along its dunes, he had felt the cool breeze against the fresh cuts and scratches caught along his arms and sides during the plunges through the brush and swamp thickets.

Diving into the water, he went out -- so far the two enemy tribesmen seemed a smaller threat as they watched from the shoreline. Finally, they came out to get him.

Perhaps it was the cool water which made an image last so long. He could remember every movement, slash and struggle as he drowned the Iroquois, each in turn. He always believed it was their clinging to their knives which enabled him to drag them down.

In all the years and battles since, it had never occurred to him that his people might be defeated; or be submerged under the foot of some other nation or group, or be deprived of their lands. But the thought intruded on him now.

Always, the other side kept coming. Always, the numbers were larger than before. He knew the number of settlers by this time in Kentucky outnumbered the Miamis five-to-one. But it was those others from the east -- buying or killing the people of the villages as they came. Always with promises, the money, the whiskey and the guns.

He had a vision of the loser -- alone as former allies and suppliers steal away -- such as the French before, then the Spanish and now the British.

But during the night, Little Turtle had decided there was one opportunity. But only one because of the limited supplies and reduced number of Indian warriors. His next step, he thought, would be to go quickly to Miamitown and lay before the many chiefs each calculated move to do in the Americans.

As he stepped onto the wet sand, the waiting Indians came quickly toward him. He had earlier decided he would not tell them at this time of the impending withdrawal of the British from the Old Northwest, or that support from any outside peoples was gone, perhaps forever.

The Miami warchief noticed the anxious expressions on the faces of the waiting braves. They told him General Anthony Wayne was finally making his move. The day before, July 28, 1794, the entire American army had moved out of Fort Greeneville and had begun a march north in the direction of Miamitown and the Indian villages along the Maumee.

"Has the Black Snake (Little Turtle still used that name for Wayne) sent bands of horse soldiers ahead of the others to strike and burn the villages," he asked.

"Only the scum go ahead," said Captain Johnny, the tall, scarred Shawnee, meaning Wayne's scouts, mostly the hated Cherokees. "The army moves in one slow body, like the old bear."

"We go quickly then by the river to the place of the Miamis," said the Turtle. Turning to the Shawnee chief, he told him to take a small party of the warriors to the vicinity of Wayne's army. "Stay near them day and night but beyond reach of their claws. Try to draw the soldiers toward the great swamp. Also, we will have need of one of their scouts -- alive."

As he proceeded towards Miamitown, the Turtle learned of Wayne's halt near Girtytown (now St. Mary's, Ohio) to build another link in his line of stockades extending up from Cincinnati. This one was named Fort Adams.

100

Carried on welcome westerly breezes, the odors of the village cook fires came to Little Turtle some distance along the river before he came to the clearing of the three rivers. It seemed to him that there was an unusual lack of activity at Miamitown, however. He could only see a few children playing a game with leg bones and an occasional squaw muttering as she reached about a fire under the supper pot.

The Miami chieftain immediately sought out several runners to gather together the chiefs of the various tribes for a council of war. He then went to the house of Antoine Lasselle, one of the French traders, for an evening meal. Later, he crossed the river to the village of Le Gris. There he was joined by his wife, the daughter of a Miami chief; his wife's younger sister and the elder of his two daughters, Sweet Breeze. She, the daughter, told the Turtle she had received no word from her husband, William Wells, since he had left for the mission to General Wayne at Greeneville many moons earlier.

Little Turtle had two sons, both of whom were dead by this time. One had died of a fever during his boyhood. The other, while still in his youth, had been struck down with gunshot wounds in a raid along the Ohio River, and following two weeks of lingering, succumbed.

Little Turtle rose early the day of the war talks. He had slept rather than palaver the previous night during which time some of the chiefs had arrived. In the cool morning light before the summer sun burned off the gentle mist along the St. Joseph River he walked for some distance upstream. He enjoyed the quiet of the day's early moments. But his main reason was one of tactics. He had found over the years that the Indian chiefs might be many, but they were prone to arrive at quick, emotional decisions. Thus, by staying away for a period from the council fire, he gave them a chance to argue and gesticulate. Then, after they had fairly talked themselves out, he could walk in and lay before them a fresh course of action, and quite likely, receive enthusiastic responses.

"The Black Snake and his soldiers come closer to our villages," said Little Turtle. "They are far more numerous than the warriors of the Indian nations, but the

101

fox need not count the rabbits. Tell your many braves we will meet with the coming of the second sunrise at the dry place near the great swamp."

The Turtle then swept his hand across the dry earth in the center of the council circle. "They are here busy cutting down the trees. As they cut, we will move east below the swamp. If we have the fortune, the soldiers will come at our villages along these same paths as those who came here before. Those paths and all the rabbits which come upon them will smell of horse meat before the next moon rises above this totem."

Most of the chiefs emitted harsh sounds of approval, and soon were on their feet and leaving Kekionga. The Turtle, however, stood for some time at the clearing. As always, he had shown a quiet sureness in his speech to the various tribal heads. Actually, an uneasiness clung to him. At about that time, he noticed a large rat near the river's edge. It had only been in the last couple years that there were rats in the Indian country.

The endurance of the Indians in the days of the Old Northwest was one of the marvels of mankind. Had the famed Greek runner of Marathon been a Miami Indian, he would not have fallen dead after his 26-mile dash to Athens. Horses were no match in long-distance tests with these children of the wilderness. There were numerous instances where Indians on foot pursued men on horses from sunrise to sundown, finally overtaking their quarry when the horses fell dead from exhaustion.

The Indians spent a good portion of their childhood and youth developing an indifference to pain and privation. So effective was the development of self control in this respect that they could be burned alive without uttering a sound or even showing a change in facial expression. Games and tests of courage were both a constant and colorful part of the young braves' daily life along the streams and in the forests. As an example of the traits developed, some of the Indians who joined Little Turtle for his bloody victory over the army of General St. Clair in 1791 traveled by foot more than 40 miles in less than a day,

102

then waited patiently, naked to the waist, as snow fell for several hours before the dawn attack.

Because of the Indian runners, communications in the Great Lakes territories and beyond were the world's fastest during the era of Indian trails and water routes. Not until the telegraph was invented and put in use the following century did the speed of message transmission catch up and exceed that which the Indians had when they held sway in unbroken length over thousands of miles of the New World.

It was one of the ironies of war in the wilderness that Little Turtle usually knew the acts of the American government at Philadelphia before the United States generals which he opposed in the field. Typically, English diplomatic staffers at the American capitol would pass along the word to officials in Canada, and the Indian runners would carry any critical information west.

Thus it was that the Turtle knew he was in a race against time in the drawing of Anthony Wayne into making a fatal mistake which could still salvage an Indian victory. The Miami warchief reasoned that once General Wayne learned of the expected success of the Jay Treaty between the United States and Great Britain, the strategic advantages would all be on the side of the Americans. Wayne would know then that there would be no help to the Indians from the British; no further arms, and no support forces from the several British forts in the Indian country.

It was in the first week of August when Little Turtle and Le Gris saw an Indian runner coming swiftly toward them. The two Miami chiefs, together with others of the Indian confederacy, had been positioning more than a thousand warriors in the swampy thickets near where the St. Mary's River crosses what is now the Indiana-Ohio state line.

The Turtle was almost startled to hear his chance calculations were so likely to bear fruit -- and very quickly, it appeared. The Indian messenger from the raiding and scouting party of Captain Johnny told the Miami warchief that troops of General Wayne were coming toward Miamitown, and were already on the path in the exact direction leading to the Indian concentrations.

The wrinkles in the face of old Le Gris creased upward and the yellow of his one eye glinted.

"The worms will remember this day. There is enough black water in this place to swallow the Black Snake and all his pretty coats," said Le Gris, having in mind Wayne's well-known inclination for fastidious and fashionable dress being smothered in the muck of the surrounding swamps.

Little Turtle sent hurriedly for any additional armed warriors which might be nearing the vicinity. Though short on rifles and ammunition, he figured surprise and the short-range sight in the thickets could make up for the lack of firepower, particularly if the army of some 3,000 soldiers could be thrown into disorder.

As the hours passed, the Indian force grew. The warriors, painted and sweating for action, slipped carefully into loosely connected hiding places over several square miles. Only an occasional call, much like an animal of the woods, could be heard as darkness came.

Little Turtle did not expect the American troops during the night hours. He originally was preparing for the invading force to move into range the previous afternoon. But when that failed to transpire, he decided the slowness of the American army might be a stroke of luck for the Indians who could use more braves.

But he soon learned it was not luck. In the dim light of early dawn, even before the awakening sounds of the summer birds, he was alerted to a small group of warriors coming through the thick growth of walnut and oak trees. He could see the blackened face of Captain Johnny and other Shawnees. He knew the answer, even before the asking of the question.

The Indian scouting party said the Americans, after coming some distance up the trail, had suddenly turned around and gone back in the direction which they had come. The Turtle nodded his head after they spoke, but stood quietly at the center of an opening in the forest. He knew at that moment the last opportunity to defeat the army of General Mad Anthony Wayne had evaporated.

Little Turtle was not in the vicinity of Fort Defiance when that strong point was constructed after Anthony

Wayne crossed up the Indians by marching directly north to the Maumee instead of attacking Miamitown further to the west.

The Miami warchief, however, would have had no trouble writing the American general's report to the U. S. Secretary of War the following week.

As the letter of August 14, 1794, shows, modesty was not one of Mad Anthony Wayne's stronger traits. Military astuteness was.

"I have the honor to inform you that the army under my command took possession of this very important post on the morning of the eighth.

"I had made such demonstrations for a length of time previously to taking up our line of march as to induce the savages to expect our advance by the route of the Miami villages, to the left, or toward Roche de Bout, by the right -- which feints appear to have produced the desired effect, by drawing the attention of the enemy to those points, and giving an opening for the army to approach undiscovered by a devious, that is, in a central direction.

"Thus, sir, we have gained possession of the grand emporium of the hostile Indians of the west without loss of blood. Everything is now prepared for a forward move tomorrow morning toward Roche de Bout, or foot of the Rapids."

Indians from a distance kept their watch along the rivers. They could see the guns of more than a thousand soldiers guarding against attack. Behind the soldiers were many others running about and dragging timbers for Fort Defiance, on a bluff overlooking the Maumee River near where the Auglaise River flows.

Fort Defiance consisted of four large stockhouses and high pointed battlements. It effectively isolated Miamitown from the east river route and cut the Indians' main road to its source of supply at Detroit.

Little Turtle had been informed many months earlier by British intelligence that the principal objective of the American army was the taking of Miamitown. It was not surprising therefore that he planned to ambush Wayne's

105

forces along that route, and fell for the "feint" Wayne mentioned in his report.

Wayne's next moves were again calculated to keep the Indians off balance. First, he planned his march east, towards Lake Erie and the British Fort Miami on the lower Maumee, instead of marching west on the major Indian center at three rivers and the string of villages in that direction. Next, he sent an emissary of peace -- always a good tactic in such circumstances.

Little Turtle and some of the other chiefs were up river from Anthony Wayne's army when a man named Christopher Miller, a former renegade who had lived in the Indian villages, was brought to the council fire under a flag of truce. In his first words, Miller made it clear that Wayne was holding Indian hostages to assure his safe return. He then handed Little Turtle a document from General Wayne.

"To the Delawares, Shawnees, Miamis and Wyandots, and to each and every one of them, and to all the other nations of Indians northwest of the Ohio," the commander's message began.

"Brothers -- Be no longer deceived or led astray by the false promises and language of the bad white men at the foot of the rapids; they have neither the power nor the inclination to help you.

"No longer shut your eyes to your true interest and happiness, nor your ears to this last overture of peace. But, in pity of your innocent women and children, come and prevent the further effusion of blood. Let them experience the kindness and friendship of the United States of America, and the invaluable blessings of peace and tranquility." Wayne asked the Indians to send delegates to meet him "to settle the preliminaries of lasting peace."

The Indians were not deceived by the peace overture of Mad Anthony Wayne. They could see in the distance the smoke from the villages in the vicinity of Fort Defiance. Not only the villages but all the crops and other things of the Indians as far as the eye could see were under the torch of the invading soldiers.

"Let me cut this dog in half," said Simon Girty as he took a step toward the emissary Miller.

Miller began in a screeching voice, "You, you can't. They'll kill you ..."

"Hold. Hold," said the Turtle. "We have further use of this man's skin." Turning to Miller, the Miami warchief said, "Go back to the Black Snake and tell him we will ponder his words. Tell him if he will wait where he is for ten days, we will send for you so that you can deliver our decision."

But even while the Indians were listening to the "peace" message, General Wayne began moving his army out of Fort Defiance and started his march down the north shore of the river towards the Maumee Rapids.

Little Turtle's answer to Anthony Wayne, suggesting the Americans wait for ten days for the decision of the Indian chiefs was no more than a bald play for time. The Miami warchief considered anything which delayed the soldiers of the United States in the land of tribes, especially with the long vulnerable supply line, might possibly work to the Indians' advantage. It was a straw in the wind which cost nothing. It didn't work, however, as General Wayne's previously-planned advance moved on schedule.

The Turtle then decided the time had come to reveal to the many chiefs a different and hard choice. A choice, he thought, which had to be made quickly -- at a meeting which soon followed.

"This is squaw talk," said the Shawnee Chief Blue Jacket in a nearly screaming voice from the far side of the council fire.

Tecumseh, standing beside Blue Jacket, drew his knife and looked menacingly across at Little Turtle. Blue Jacket, however, put a staying hand on the arm of Tecumseh and directed his attention toward Buckongahelas, the chief of the Delawares, who had stood up to address the Indians at the war parley near the banks of the Maumee.

Of all the Indian nations which had been fighting under the leadership of the Miami warchief Little Turtle, the Delawares were the most numerous. Despite some arguments over land rights, Buckongahelas had always

107

supported the Turtle since his tribe had been allowed to settle in the Miami territory after the Delawares were forced out of their ancestorial lands to the east.

Little Turtle, who moments earlier had astounded the gathering of chiefs by suggesting they avoid battle with the army of Anthony Wayne, waited passively to hear what the Delaware chief had to say.

"We have followed you many times on the path of war and returned many times with the scalps of the enemy. Our young men have gone in the snows and over the rivers. They have waited in the night and some have forever been lost to their women and their little ones. But our people have survived. Only in this land have we been able to defeat those who came against us. Only here have we been able to build our villages and have a place for our old ones, our women and our children. The warriors of the Delawares are brave and ready to attack the soldiers of the American general."

Chief Crane of the Wyandots and Little Otter of the Ottawas gave yells of agreement. Winnemac, chief of the Potawatomis, also called for a strike against the U. S. invaders.

The Turtle stepped closer to the fire light. "Let them burn the villages. Let them burn the fort of the English yonder towards the great lake. When the snow flies, we will still be here. When their soldiers return to their homes, it will be our turn to burn. Let them build their wooded buildings and cut down the trees now. I, the warchief of the Miamis, say wait.

"The army of the Black Snake now marches down our river. They have many soldiers and many guns. We are not so strong now. If the warriors of the Indian nations are defeated, who then can walk with the pride of our ancestors."

The suggestion of the possibility of being defeated tasted bitter to most of the chiefs. Several began muttering "rabbit" and "squaw" -- words denoting cowardice to the Indians.

Other considerations came into play. While Little Turtle hoped Wayne would attack the British Fort Miami on the lower Maumee, thus possibly upsetting peace negotiations between the English and the Americans, others present had things to protect.

"Only a victory now can save the Indians," said Alexander McKee, a British agent with a house and trading post near the English fort. Other white men who urged immediate attack were Simon Girty and Matthew Elliott, both renegades from American territory, and Jacques and Antoine Lasselle, who had trading buildings at Miamitown.

There was a hoarse cough from one side of the circle. The council grew quiet. Old Le Gris stood staring at the white men. He did not like even sympathetic outsiders injecting themselves into Indian parleys. They drew back into the shadows.

Le Gris, who was a mysterious and feared figure even among the chiefs, let his one eye gaze around the council. When he spoke, all leaned forward to hear.

"My brother, the Turtle, took us to victories as far as the high falls to the east and the great rivers to the south and west. Three times in our own lands our warriors did as he spoke, and struck down the enemy as never before in all the times of the Indians.

"But he also said never again will the Indian nations let the American invaders come putting torches to our villages, scattering our people. Yet even on this day there is the evil smell of smoke in the air. There are the cries and wails among the trees from this place to the Auglaise.

"As the wolf goes out to cut the belly of the stag, we shall go now." Taking out a knife, Le Gris cut into the wrinkled skin of his long bare arm. He caught blood in the palm of his hand and threw it into the faces of some of the chiefs.

"Let the first blood on your hands be mine; but let the last be that of the Black Snake."

Shouts went up with the fire and smoke of the council circle. The Indians, most already painted for war, immediately began moving toward an anticipated blood bath of Anthony Wayne.

Two figures remained in the fire light. "I will kill that boy," said Le Gris.

The Turtle looked at Le Gris, but said nothing. Le Gris had never liked William Wells, the Turtle's adopted son.

By now, the Turtle guessed, Wells had permanently joined the Americans as a scout. In fact, no sooner had Wells become familiar with Wayne's strength then he saw the wisdom of joining the winning side.

Little Turtle was basically a calculating man. Later, as he weighed the possible outcome of the looming battle of the Indian tribes with the army of Anthony Wayne, foul alternatives played on his mind. Neither the clarity of the blue summer sky nor the warmth of the morning sun salved his mood.

The Miami warchief had told the leaders of the many Indian nations that it would be a mistake to attack the marching army of General Wayne as it moved down the Maumee. When the others turned their backs on the Turtle and his tactic for stalling, they chose Blue Jacket, the Shawnee chief, and Turkey Foot of the Ottawa to lead the warrior army.

The Miami Indians split over the issue. The Kekiongas under Le Gris chose to do battle. The Eel River and Wabash Miamis withdrew with the Turtle, as did most of the remaining Chippewas, Mingoes and Kickapoos. The attacking force of about 1,500 Indians consisted of the Delawares, Shawnees, some Miamis, the Ottawas, the Wyandots and a few Potawatomis. There were also a handful of the Canadian militia and a few French traders.

Speculating on the future possibilities, the Turtle came to three conclusions. If the Indians were victorious, he would look the fool. If they were defeated, Wayne would proceed over a wide area to raze the Indian villages and take into his grip the entire Maumee vicinity -- something which would likely happen even if the Indians avoided battle, but with one very important difference. Little Turtle still had before his eyes a possible result he had voiced to the many chiefs. If the Indians were routed by Mad Anthony Wayne, they would have little power for future days -- no weight in negotiations, and even after all the great victories in the past years, they would end up a defeated people.

As he watched the swirling waters of the Maumee, an

odd feeling of detachment came over him. If there was disappointment, there was also relief at no longer being the center of every decision. And he also understood how difficult it had been for many Indians to play his waiting game for months on end. Their temper was more at home in action and the quick pursuit.

Floating down the current in the river was a colorful bit of wood which caught the Turtle's eye. It was a small Indian toy, perhaps from Miamitown some 80 miles upstream.

He turned to several Miamis near the river bank and told them to return to Miamitown and tell the villagers to begin an evacuation to places far removed and safe from destruction, which he thought was almost sure to follow the approaching conflict. Then, when most of the Miami party had left, he told about a dozen Mingoes and Kickapoos to come with him.

The Turtle and the small party crossed to the south side of the Maumee and proceeded down river toward the rapids, where the main body of Indians had taken up positions. Though he had spoken against the battle and said he would not participate in it, he was now deeply curious and had decided to watch from the other side of the river.

The Miami warchief already knew the Indians under Blue Jacket and Turkey Foot had been waiting for some time for the advance of the American army. The Turtle considered it the height of folly for the Indians to take up set positions in the face of an army the size of Wayne's - nearly 3,000 men, including cavalry. The warriors did, however, have the protection of dense woods and some large trees which had been flattened in a huge tangle by a recent tornado.

When Little Turtle approached the area of the fallen timbers, he could hear a few popping sounds of flintlock rifles. The battle of August 10, 1794, was already underway.

Looking across the Maumee, the Turtle's eye was drawn to a battalion of mounted riflemen on the north bank of the river. They were sweeping directly towards the Indians. The warriors behind the fallen trees met this assault with

111

heavy fire.   Soon, the cavalry slowed, then swinging around, went into a retreat.   The Indians under Blue Jacket were apparently winning the first stroke of the battle.

But, just as the horsemen began falling back from the Indian emplacement, the Turtle could see new and rapid movements coming from Wayne's main body of troops. Heading into the woods to the left of the retreating men was a large force of cavalrymen who soon went out of sight on an apparent course around the Indians' position.

Within minutes, another cavalry group came rattling along the river's edge, some splashing the shallow water, and headed for the other flank of the warriors.   In the meantime, infantrymen with long spindly bayonets attached to their rifles were advancing slowly through the tall grass.   They were still out of range, but were moving directly at the Indians, who mostly hidden were still waiting in the protection of the fallen trees.

Little Turtle continued down river on the opposite bank, going pretty much as the pace of battle went in that direction.   He could see in the distance the British stockade, Fort Miami.

It was very quiet in that quarter.   The stockade doors were closed.   He knew there were more than 400 English soldiers in that garrison, but no activity could be seen.

Though the Battle of Fallen Timbers began well enough for the Indians, Little Turtle saw the fatal situation.   From across the Maumee near the rapids, he could barely hear the rifle fire because of a rather stiff wind from the west and the noise of water tumbling through the rocks of the stream.

But he could see that most of the Indians were strung along the fallen trees and brush not far from the river's north shore.   The Turtle had a sudden urge to cross the river and tell the warriors to go for the trees and heavy thickets further from the river, leaving but a token force in the area which had been swept by the tornado.   In the woods, the Indians would have some chances of ambushing the American horsemen.

The thought then struck the Miami chieftain that this possibility was exactly what General Wayne had anticipated, and was the reason for his initial probe by having a battalion of cavalry attack the Indian concentration in the timbers. He wanted to see if most of the warriors were in fact really there. Finding that to be the case, the American general proceeded to dispatch mounted forces to the right and to the left. He then directed his infantry legions to move up through the high grass and weeds in front of the Indians.

The cavalry along the water's edge and the infantrymen drew the fire of the warriors, still hidden and protected by the fallen trees and brush and trunks of the tangle. While a large portion of the Indians were attempting to reload the gunpowder and lead balls into their single-shot rifles, the American regulars made a dash at them with bayonets. From across the river, the Turtle could see several of the Indians ducking away from the front area. Shortly, many more began to run. Perhaps partly because they didn't have time to reload.

The battle continued in hide-and-seek fashion for nearly two miles through the heavily-wooded area. Little Turtle knew the firearms and ammunition of the Indians were limited to what little they were able to get from the British. He was not surprised when they began to disperse.

The battle had lasted for only about an hour. The large group of mounted militia under General Charles Scott, which Wayne had sent to the left for a circuitous route through the forest to hit the flank or rear of the Indians, had hardly seen any action. Either the warriors fell back before expected, or the mounted riflemen, some 1,600 strong, got lost in the wilderness for a time.

Wayne described the crucial moment in his report: "Such was the impetuousity of the charge of the first line of the infantry, that the Indians and Canadian militia and volunteers were drove from all their coverts in so short of time, that, although every possible exertion was used by the officers of the second line of the legion, and by Generals Scott, Todd and Barbee, of the mounted volunteers, to gain their proper positions, but part of each could get up in season to participate in the action; the enemy being drove, in the course of one hour, more than two miles through the thick woods."

113

The battle ended with the arrival of Mad Anthony Wayne's forces at the clearing in front of the British garrisoned Fort Miami. The American losses in the conflict at Fallen Timbers amounted to 45 killed and about 100 wounded. The Indian losses, including the Canadian volunteers, totaled about 85 killed and about 200 wounded or injured.

For sustained violence, the Battle of Fallen Timbers was in no way comparable to the overwhelming victory of Little Turtle against General Arthur St. Clair three years earlier; or even the Turtle's repulse of General Joshua Harmar's troops in 1790 at Miamitown. American losses at the St. Clair debacle alone were 20 times those of Wayne's army along the Maumee.

As far as the Indians were concerned, their numbers in the strike against Fort Recovery were perhaps double the warrior count which waited for Wayne's advance on Fallen Timbers.

Chief Little Turtle, together with his small party of Kickapoo and Mingo braves, followed the troops of Anthony Wayne as they took up positions around Fort Miami. He then watched what he considered Wayne's first rash act. The American general and an aide, Lt. William Henry Harrison, rode their horses up to the very walls of the British stockade, which held 450 British soldiers.

If the British would shoot down Wayne, the Turtle thought, it would have the effect of putting a cloud of smoke over an otherwise clear victory for the United States. But as he watched from the distance, he could only see what seemed like a short conversation between Wayne and a figure on top the fort's wall. The two Americans then turned their horses and returned to the main body of the army. It was concluded by the Miami warchief that both Wayne and the British commandant were aware of the impending treaty between England and the United States. The British did not come to the support of the Indians during the battle, and Wayne did not attack Fort Miami.

Little Turtle turned to his companions. "It will be a long winter. We have seen enough here. We go now before the darkness."

And dark was the sky for three days as the army of Anthony Wayne burned or otherwise destroyed the buildings and plantings of the Indians from Lake Erie to Fort Defiance.

Chapter 11

The difference between Sherman's march to the sea and Wayne's march from Lake Erie to Miamitown is 70 years and the fact that the Indians of the Miami nation were short of poets.

The culture of the Indians, at home with both the delicate balance of the wilderness and some loose trade with the outside civilizations, reached a high point along the Maumee and Wabash Rivers. Here were the many tribes which founded villages in great number. They were as independent and self-sufficient as any people can be.

One of Wayne's soldiers, Lt. John Boyer, gave an eye-witness account of the Fort Defiance area, where he first arrived at the Maumee (a place which today is in the state of Ohio):

"This place far excels in beauty any in the western country, and believed equalled by none in the Atlantic States. Here are vegetables of every kind in abundance, and we marched four or five miles in corn fields down the Auglaize and there are not less than one thousand acres of corn round the town. The land in general is of the fir nature.

"This country appears well adapted for the enjoyment of industrious people, who cannot avoid living in as great luxury as in any place throughout the states, nature having lent a most beautiful hand in the arrangement of the position, that a man can send the produce to market in his own boat. The land level and river is navigable, not more than 60 miles from the lake."

Similar things could have been said about many acres for hundreds of miles. But the end of it all was in sight. Never again would Indians in North America create and maintain a strong, independent wilderness society such as was threatened, then destroyed, in Little Turtle's lifetime. Romantic stories and movies would later lend some colorful status to the Indians of the American Wild West;

but in fact, such groups seldom prospered beyond scrub living and warparty raids against stray cavalry companies.

After Wayne's army of 3,000 regulars and mounted militia spent a few days razing the area around what is today Toledo and Maumee, Ohio, the troops began their march to the west.

A campaign of scorched earth swept up the Maumee Valley as far as Fort Defiance, and after a short rest, continued again in the direction of Miamitown. Everything which might later support Indian life was destroyed. Villages were burned, one after the other, as the soldiers moved both along the river and for many miles inland on either side.

Now that the United States had the upper hand in the Old Northwest, it was Wayne's job to see that the federal grip became a permanent one. It was a far cry from the situation only two years before, when Congress was considering leaving the territory to the Indians after the Turtle's bloody destruction of the armies of St. Clair and Harmar. Only because of President Washington's firm insistance on a new campaign to make way for western expansion was the third expedition provided.

The ultimate aim of each of the campaigns was Miamitown. It was believed that this was the necessary key to the breaking of the confederated Indian armies. A relatively cleared area, the three rivers community included seven villages of three different Indian nations, plus an active group of traders, both French and Canadian. More importantly, the thriving area was seen by the U. S. Government as the main staging ground for the allied Indians who were capable of dispatching thousands of warriors against entire armies, and launching raiding parties which were the terror of pioneer settlements from Pennsylvania to the Mississippi. No similar Indian community was ever known to have existed before or since north of the Rio Grande.

As the fire and smoke moved toward Kekionga, the Indian population and everyone else began a mass exodus.

117

Among those fleeing was the young white woman, Frances Slocum, who as a little five-year old, had been kidnapped by Indians in Pennsylvania nearly 20 years earlier, and who wouldn't be found by her relatives for another 39 years.

Others included the Girty brothers, James and George, several dozen French families, and any English sympathizers in the area. The Indians moved in many directions -- some to the rivers to the south and west; others to Lake Michigan and Chicago village, a Miami concentration of old but now numerous with the Potawatomi.

Wayne described the final leg of the invasion in his journal: "The legion began their march for the Miami villages whither they arrived at 5 p.m. on the 17th of September, 1794, and the following day the troops fortified their camps, while the commander-in-chief reconnoitered the ground and determined on the spot to build a garrison."

The systematic reduction of every building and crop in sight of the spot was begun. In the coming months and years, very few of the Indians or traders ever moved back to the vicinity. The Miamitown which was a center of wilderness society and trade was gone forever. And it would be a full generation before any sizeable community would again arise at the three rivers. This would be with the settling of the pioneers and immigration from abroad. But a fort was established -- Fort Wayne.

While Anthony Wayne and his legions were busy building a stockade, the tribes of the Miami Confederation were running about like parts of an injured centipede.

Some of the parts gravitated to the banks of the Maumee River a few miles from the present city of Toledo. There the various chiefs exchanged insults across the council fires and took turns accusing one or the other of fault in the defeat at Fallen Timbers. As the nights grew long, there would be an occasional speech about how the Indians would slaughter the American army at some future attack.

Chief Little Turtle did not join the some 1,600 Indians which had gathered for the palaver. He did, however, go in that direction on his way to a meeting with the British and several of the chiefs near the Detroit River. With him was a party of Eel River and Wabash Miamis, the Kickapoos and several Illinois Indians.

As they moved down the Maumee they were struck visually by the wide desolation left by the American forces which had come through the valley two weeks earlier. Not only the villages and corn had been put to the torch, but even the trees of the orchards had been cut and the vegetables in the ground had been destroyed.

The warriors still had the smell of smoke in their nostrils when they approached Fort Defiance. As they emerged from the trees by the Auglaise, they saw some 20 soldiers across the clearing. The uniformed men were outside the stockade and possibly 100 yards away from the gate.

It was not a case of love at first sight. There was a momentary stillness as the Indians and soldiers stared at each other. Then, as if a starting gun had been sounded, a life-and-death foot race began.

The Turtle waved a portion of the warriors in the direction of the fort's gate in an attempt to head off the men. The Indians tossed aside anything other than their knives as they started to sprint across the clearing.

Some of the soldiers -- those fast of foot or closer to the stockade -- won their contests and their lives. Eleven were not so fortunate. In the open, not more than a dozen yards from the walls of the fort, they were cut down quickly -- seconds before their yells could bring protective fire from the garrison. Two young recruits among the soldiers, who otherwise would have made it to the gate, had taken the time to pick up some valued possession, and thus their lives were ended on the grassy wilderness bank of the Maumee.

The Indians moved swiftly on. A group of mounted riflemen, coming out of the fort in pursuit a few minutes later, never established contact with the Turtle's party which melted into the woods.

Further down the river, the Indians became aware of the approach of another party of warriors coming from the opposite direction. The Turtle soon recognized Le Gris and Chief Pacan at the head of a large group of Miamis. It was

119

the first time since the acrimonious council before the defeat at Fallen Timbers that the Turtle had found himself in the proximity of Le Gris.

The Turtle's nephew, Jean Baptiste Richardville, talked briefly with Pacan and was told the group was on its way to Kekionga to watch the movements of Wayne's army. Little Turtle and Le Gris, however, passed without exchanging a word.

Le Gris approached Miamitown with caution. The party moved north from the Maumee River, swinging around to the St. Joseph River. There was no question of attacking the American troops. Though General Wayne had already sent the 1,600 men of the Kentucky militia back to Fort Greeneville, there remained in the immediate vicinity nearly 2,000 soldiers.

The Indians did, however, creep along the St. Joseph as far as the remains of the old Fort Miami which had been originally built by the French and was later occupied by the British until taken by the Indians during the Pontiac uprising 30 years prior to Wayne's coming.

With his eye between two warped boards, Le Gris could see down the river to where the new fort was being erected. Work had started more than a week earlier. The outside walls of the stockade were already up and many men were crawling about, particularly where numerous notched logs were being fitted for stockhouses.

Others were clearing away every vestige of brush, tree or Indian hovel from a wide space around the fort. Le Gris' eyewent up from the water to the slight hill where the fort stood. It was across from the outflow of the St. Joseph and about 100 yards south of the bend of the St. Mary's River. The fort commanded a clear view of the source of the Maumee River. Several cannons were being hoisted to placements which faced in that direction. Le Gris also noticed that all seven of the Indian villages in the vicinity were little more than charred remains.

For all the activity, there was a peculiar stillness, perhaps due to the extreme cold for so early in the season. Late in the afternoon, snow began to fall, carried by winds from the northwest. Le Gris and his party moved further up the river following a trail toward the lake country, where many of the women and children had gone.

Mad Anthony Wayne, now 49 years old, stared out over the chill landscape. The trees already had deep October hues, and a freakishly-early winter wind brought snow flurries across the river and about the stockade.

His hand went instinctively to his injured side as he stepped carefully along the new catwalk of the fort, still under construction at Miamitown. He then saw something along the distant bank of the St. Joseph River which gave him a start.

The tall almost-cadaverous figure of an Indian was slowly shuffling away from the old French fort. Soon, several more warriors could be seen stepping lightly, then perhaps a dozen more.

Wayne shouted for the sentry. "Where in deuce are the patrols and scouts. I can see hostiles only a half mile over there," he said lifting a finger in the direction of the St. Joseph.

The general waited impatiently as a group of horsemen took long minutes getting underway. He watched as they went across the Maumee and up the riverbank at a gallop.

Wayne was annoyed further by their report when they returned. The patrol had found no trace of the Indians. Only two bodies. Apparently, a pair of soldiers had grown careless. They were cut beyond recognition. Neither had fired the warning shots as required by all on duty in the fort area.

A chill sense of lineliness came over Wayne. He would be glad when he was away from this place. His army was desperately short of supplies, and an early onset of winter was a cruel stroke. From high overhead there was an odd honking sound. It was coming from someplace above the grey clouds. These must be the migrating Canadian geese he had once read about.

As he looked, there was an opening in the grey and he could see a V-formation moving south across the blue. Wayne decided he would be moving in the same direction

121

as soon as possible.

After going down into a stockade room, which smelled of the fresh oak timbers, Wayne sat himself carefully at his desk. He could feel the pain of gout in his foot and his internal bleeding was worse each day. He quickly wrote out instruction to Col. John Hamtramck for the fort dedication ceremonies -- to be read October 22, naming the garrison after himself to the accompaniment of 15 rounds of cannon fire.

He had had a premonition of death for many weeks. "Under those impressions and the uncertain events of war, I have devised in the best manner I can all my estate, both real and personal, to my son and daughter, and appoint you, my son and Mrs. Lewis my executors," he had written to a friend in Pennsylvania.

It was not only his injuries, received when he was nearly killed by a falling tree on the march to the Maumee, which concerned Wayne. Nor were the hostile Indians his only problem.

By this time, Anthony Wayne was completely aware of a plot by General James Wilkinson, his second in command, to get rid of him. Wilkinson and James Hawkins, a Kentucky land speculator and contractor, had been trying to sabotage Wayne's campaign by delaying supplies and sending critical messages to influential politicians in the east. Though Wayne knew of Wilkinson's efforts to succeed him as commander of the west, he could not prove it. This tended to make Wayne sour and distrustful.

To protect himself, Anthony Wayne played one subordinate off against the other. He named as his adjutant one Captain Edward Butler, the puffed-up and mean younger brother of General Richard Butler, the harsh soldier who died in St. Clair's defeat. The younger Butler did his job too well. Fear and hate walked with Wayne's army. Discipline was heavy, uneven and breaking.

Even Colonel Hamtramck was bitter, and wrote to an acquaintance: "No doubt about it, the old man really is mad."

Captain John Cooke in his diary tells of "three men deserted from the First Legion and a few days later eleven men have actually deserted and eight more are missing, either killed, deserted or taken."

Cooke, two days afterward, said "A man deserted from Captain Thompson's company, now commanded by Captain Bines. This desertion seems extraordinary after McClellan's report to the commander that he had, in accordance with orders, killed one of the deserts he was after and had seen two more who were killed and scalped."

On the same day, Cooke reported four or five men, sent to Greeneville for supplies, had been killed, and "Nelly Bundy was taken at the same time."

But in spite of the bleeding, plots, desertions and near starvation rations, Wayne held firm. He told no one of his plans -- ordering moves by sudden announcements. The one-time young hero of the Revolution and ladies' man of Philadelphia drawing rooms turned to the iron hand for survival at the place which today bears his name.

In this way, the days passed and the work of the Republic in the wilderness proceeded. The soldiers were numerous, and always cautious. They were never alone.

The heavy black cloud overhead matched the mood of Le Gris. The old chief had returned to his "blackberry patch" and found someone else in possession.

Kekionga, an ancient Indian word meaning the place of the blackberries, was the chief village of the Miamis. And in Kekionga, Le Gris was the chief Indian.

Seemingly ageless, the halt and one-eyed chief had seen them all come and go. He remembered the early French adventurers and the missionaries, who were followed by traders who set up permanent houses by the Miamitown rivers and portage. And he remembered when the French soldiers were driven out by the English.

It was Le Gris who had frightened a pretty Indian maiden into enticing the young English commandant out of old Fort Miami and to his death 30 years before during the Pontiac War.

Later, when Pontiac came to Miamitown to establish himself, Le Gris dampened the enthusiasm of the young braves and stolidly put the palm up to the famous warrior. "The great chief of the Ottawas will find hunting grounds in the distance down the river," he said at the time. And Pontiac went. He founded a village along the Maumee in the direction of Lake Erie, but was killed four years later while on a trip in the Mississippi area.

When the English went to war against the colonies, Le Gris used his strange arts of persuasion on the other chiefs to convince them that Little Turtle should be warchief of all the Miami villages. Warchief was a separate rank among the Miamis from the hereditary tribal chiefs such as Le Gris.

He had earlier seen the Little Turtle, the half-Mohican from Eel River, could grasp both the tactics needed for Indian victories and also the wider political strategems of the enemy powers. His choice was vindicated. The Turtle quickly won a series of wilderness battles and later, when the warchief put together the great Miami Confederation of most of the Indian nations of the Old Northwest, he led the warriors to chilling slaughters of two American armies.

But now, the Indians had been defeated. As he looked across the clearing to the far side of the river, Le Gris could see the invaders putting the finishing touches on a fort. They were doing this in the place which had always been his, and his people's. His bony fingers went white with hate, but his facial muscles hardly moved. As the sunless day gave way to darkness, Le Gris did not stir. He was still standing there when the sun rose the next morning.

The old Indian immediately sensed there was something different about the fort on this morning. He had studied every oak board in the stockade and looked for any weakness. He knew the very sounds of the army routine. The new activity around the stronghold quickened his interest.

Presently, six formations of soldiers were marching across the grounds in front of the fort. Standing up on the wall was a figure in fancy uniform and cockaded hat. Le Gris could not see well enough to make out the features of the face, but knew it was General Anthony Wayne.

The soldiers then marched in through the stockade gates. After a few minutes, Le Gris could hear bits of loud

124

speech, and see a flag being raised on a pine pole. There were some cheers. Then the sound of cannon fire echoed across the three rivers and down the valley. Le Gris counted 15 reports.

Five days later, the man in the hat with the cockade rode out of Fort Wayne. It was October 27, 1794, and General Anthony Wayne led the main portion of his army south along the trace of General Harmar. He left behind a garrison force of about 300 men under Colonel John Hamtramck. Mad Anthony Wayne would never return to the place.

"After four and half miles we came to a large swamp," reported Captain John Cooke. But the army found the high ground which others had previously followed through the swamp lands. After two more days they reached the St. Mary's River, then going south, they arrived at Greeneville on Nov. 2.

Neither Le Gris or any other Indians made an attempt to attack Wayne's army on its march south. Le Gris knew the many tribes were too scattered, nor did they have the arms at the moment to start the war dances.

The Old chief had heard that Wayne was already circulating spies and scouts among the Indians, trying to convince them to meet him in a grand council the following year at Fort Greeneville.

But as he cast his eye around the charred area which had once been his home, Le Gris began to weigh one more possibility. This would be a better place for the great council gathering. If he could entice the American general back to this remote source of the Maumee, Le Gris thought, the fires of old might blow in a different direction. After awhile, he went in a northerly direction, slowly disappearing beyond a slight rise.

The strange dance of the spawning fish, which were rippling the surface of the Detroit River, amused the Indians along the shore of Grosse Ile. As far as the eye could see, the silvery creatures were splashing and flashing in the morning sun.

Little Turtle laughed, and after watching a little longer,

turned and began walking across the island. The others followed. They went over the narrow channel to the mainland, then a short distance south to a Wyandot village called Brownstown, where the Huron River joins the Detroit.

The British delegation was already there, as were many of the Indian chiefs -- Blue Jacket of the Shawnees, Buckongahelas of the Delawares, White Pigeon of the Potawatomis, The Crane of the Wyandots and Brant of the Mohawks.

John Graves Simcoe, governor of Upper Canada (Ontario), had asked the chiefs to meet with him at a "great council fire." Presumably, the British were quite aware of the Indian loss of confidence in their support, a natural result of British inactivity at Fallen Timbers. The idea of the council was to patch things up a bit.

But Little Turtle already knew there was little to be expected from the talks. He had learned through sources in Quebec that Simcoe was under Foreign Office instructions to promise nothing of substance. The prime interest of the English was the successful conclusion of the Jay Treaty with the United States, which among other things, was designed to keep the Americans from joining on the side of France in a war which was going on in Europe at the time. As for the territories, the English wanted to maintain a quiet hand.

Some of the Indians, on the other hand, came to the council expecting that arms and provisions would be furnished so they could renew hostilities in the defense of their lands and villages.

As Little Turtle entered the council circle, Chief Brant was already giving one of his speeches. The Turtle was glad he had taken his time getting there. Better yet, he wished he had delayed a little longer or that the attempt to cut Brant's throat some years earlier had been successful. Brant, as a member of the pacified Iroquois League, had been dead weight to the Indians for many moons. In his speech at the meeting, he was telling the other Indians they should have taken his advice in coming to terms with the United States and he was berating the British for not giving the Indians sufficient help.

Governor Simcoe, in his address to the Indians, said "His Majesty's Government takes a fatherly interest in his sons and brothers of the Indian nations." He urged the chiefs to continue support of the British, but to hold back for the time being from any large-scale hostilities.

The Turtle insisted that Simcoe explain to the Indians at the council the meaning of treaty negotiations which had been underway in London. "Let us all hear from our big brother, the good governor, what the Indian position will be, and what we can expect now in our war with the enemy."

There was a rumble of disapproval around the council when the chiefs heard that the British would not provide new rifles and ammunition, without which the Indians would be ineffective against the Americans. Also, Simcoe said he could furnish little in the way of food and other provisions, desperately needed by many Indian families.

Tempers around the great fire grew so heated with further disclosures by Simcoe that some of the British guard from the Detroit garrison moved closer to the governor. Simcoe, forced by Little Turtle, told of one expected result of the Jay Treaty -- that the British forts in the Old Northwest would be turned over to the United States in another year or so. To the Indians, this meant the English were trading away the Indian lands to the Americans, without even giving the Indians a part in the treaty negotiations. At the most critical time in their history, the Indians were being left without any outside support or source of arms to defend themselves, their lands and way of life.

The council along the shore of the Detroit River broke up with a rash of curses and bitterness. The Crane, chief of the Erie Wyandots, looked directly at the English governor. "The Huron now go to the place of the enemy. They can hardly be worse than our friends."

"There is no hurry," the Turtle said with disinterest to The Crane.

But the Wyandots, whose villages were concentrated in the Detroit area and along the shores of Lake Huron and Lake Erie, arrived in Greeneville a few weeks later in that fall of 1794. General Wayne welcomed The Crane. He told the Indians very bluntly he had the might to destroy all the tribes, if they did not make peace.

Wayne played effectively on the disappointments of the various tribes. He said to the Wyandots they were "made fools of by the English," who told them to fight but didn't have the power to help them. He informed The Crane he would be generous to him and that the Wyandots could live in peace within the United States.

The wedge between the Indian tribes was driven. The Crane remained steadfast in favoring the negotiating of a peace treaty in the face of other chiefs who wanted to hold out for a possible new war campaign. Among other things, The Crane warned Anthony Wayne that Le Gris would try to trick the Americans into returning to Fort Wayne for the grand treaty council.

Far from the cool villages and empty corn fields where the Indians were gathered to discuss their survival, events in faraway cities and beyond the ocean were playing a part.

President Washington on Nov. 19, 1794, rose before the joint assembly of the Senate and House for his Sixth Annual Address.

"The intelligence from the army under the command of General Wayne is a happy presage to our military operations against the hostile Indians north of the Ohio. From the advices which have been forwarded, the advance which he has made must have dampened the ardor of the savages and weakened their obstinancy in waging war against the United States.

"And yet, even at this late hour, when our power to punish them cannot be questioned, we shall not be unwilling to cement a lasting peace upon the terms of candor, equity and good neighborhood."

It was a coincidence that on the same day Washington was addressing the joint houses of Congress at Philadelphia, diplomats in London were affixing their signatures to a document which would be known as the Jay Treaty or London Treaty. Among other things, it almost led to war between the United States and France, repudiated several earlier agreements, called for trade concessions between the U. S. and England, and called for peace between the U. S. and England in the Great Lakes frontier area.

According to the treaty, the British were to surrender their western forts to the Americans by June 1, 1796. These strong points were at Detroit, Mackinac, along the Maumee and on the shores of Lake Erie. If anyone considered the Indians might have rights to the land where they had lived for generations, it was not mentioned in the documents.

Also on the same day, Secretary of War Henry Knox received a letter from General Anthony Wayne. In it, Wayne emphasized a position he had taken weeks earlier: "Unless effectual measures are immediately adopted by both Houses for raising troops to garrison the Western posts, we have fought, bled and conquered in vain. The fertile country we are now in possession of will again become a range to the hostile aborigines of the West, who, meeting no barrier, the frontier inhabitants will fall an easy prey to a fierce and savage enemy whose tender mercies are cruelty; and who will improve the opportunity to desolate and lay waste all the settlements on the margin of the Ohio, and which they will be able to effect with impunity, unless some speedy and proper measures are adopted to re-engage the remnant of the legion."

A few days earlier, General Wayne had warned the War Department that "It would appear that the savages are playing an artful game; they have certainly met with Governor Simcoe, Colonel McKee and Captain Brant at the mouth of the Detroit River.

"It is understood by all, however, that there shall be a temporary suspension of hostilities for one moon, say until the 22nd; in fact, it has been a continued suspension upon their own part ever since the action of August 20, except for a few light predatory parties."

Wayne insisted on the maintaining of a regular army of 2,000 men on the western frontier, rather than depending on the militia. He told the Washington Administration of the need for a string of supply bases to support Fort Defiance and Fort Wayne.

"Add to this that it would afford a much better chain for the general protection of the frontiers, which, with a block house at the landing place on the Wabash eight miles southwest of the post at the Miami villages (Fort Wayne) would give us possession of all portages between the heads of the navigable waters of the Gulfs of Mexico and St. Lawrence, and serve as a barrier between the different tribes of aborigines settled along the margins of the rivers.

"But sir, all this labor and expense of blood and treasure will be rendered abortive, and of none effect, unless speedy and efficient measures are adopted by the National Legislature to raise troops to garrison those posts."

Many commanding soldiers, after success in the field, would have returned for honors and health intact. But it was Anthony Wayne's fidelity to his cause which continued the dominant American presence and frustrated the calculated hopes of Little Turtle and Le Gris. It was clear that Wayne was preparing for continued possible warfare. This and other elements were the difference. Within weeks, the combination of bitter winter winds across the scarred and hungry lands and the report of the British pullout was to further shake the unity and resolve of the Indians.

Chapter 12

Little Turtle, as he led his horse in a slow walk through the snow drift near the Tippecanoe River, could not hear President Washington refer to the Indians as savages, nor General Wayne use the term aborigines.

But his mind was drawn to the same subject. He was coming to the conclusion that neither the American government nor the English government saw the Indians as people. Things which had happened the past several months had begun to change ideas he had had since childhood.

Always before, during the many years of relations with the French and then the British, there had been the mutual agreements. The Indians traded furs and some other services for guns, cloth and various things of need, or simply items they wanted. There seemed to be respect and even fear where the others' rights were concerned. Particularly with the French, the Miamis had long association and fruitful relationships. As an example, Little Turtle's sister, Tacumwa was married to a Frenchman, as were some others, particularly those engaged in the trading business.

Yet, the treaty between the United States and Great Britain did not even recognize the existence of the Indians. They were on the land but were given no more weight than the fox or rabbit or the buffalo.

Suddenly, the Turtle changed the direction of his animal and headed east, in search of Le Gris and Pacan. He had come to a decision which would prove fateful. He had decided to talk with the other chiefs about coming to terms with the Americans. He reasoned that the Indians had failed to convince the invaders that they were people with rights and a way of life that could be respected, and that they could live in peace with neighboring white settlements.

Several things went to make up the Turtle's thinking.

There was the simple fact that the choices were limited, after the lost battle and lack of guns and provisions. This temporary military weakness led the Miami warchief to give more weight to the arguments of Antoine and Jacques Lasselle and his son-in-law, William Wells.

Antoine Lasselle had been captured by Wayne's troops at Fallen Timbers. At a subsequent court marshall, he was expecting the death penalty. He noticed, however, that the chief magistrate, Colonel Hamtramck, was wearing a ring. Lasselle gave him the masonic signal. He was acquited.

When he and his brother, Jacques, later came back to the Indian country, they told the Miamis and others that Wayne was powerful but truly wanted peace with the Indians and would be generous in granting them their traditional hunting grounds. Wells echoed these sentiments and told Little Turtle, since he was a recognized leader, he would be especially compensated.

Little Turtle had seen too much of past treaty deals to believe in the value of "grants." But, he thought, if the Indians could make a show of unity, and get themselves recognized officially as a nation, they would be able to hold their own and most of their lands.

What Chief Little Turtle could not know and could not foresee was that it was far more convenient for the Americans to not see the Indians as people. The Turtle, in his wildest dreams, would not have pictured the next three generations of frontier politicians. Their most constant and most successful campaign cries would be "I promise to clear out the savages." The age of land lust was underway.

The Turtle stayed a night at his village along Eel River, then continued his journey the following day toward the lake country. Most of the Miamis had moved north from Kekionga. Generally, they were not so destitute as the Shawnees and Delawares to the south and east.

Old Le Gris, despite the winter cold, was sitting in front of a deerskin house as the Turtle came across the frozen lake. The village was along the shore of a large pond which today straddles the Indiana-Michigan state border and is called Lake George.

132

Though the two chiefs had not exchanged a word since before the Battle of Fallen Timbers the previous August, they recognized each other with the Indian greeting of raised hands.

Little Turtle spoke first. He asked the old chief about action around the newly-constructed Fort Wayne and about the location of warriors in the area. He then told Le Gris of his thoughts about a treaty with the Americans.

"When the stags stand together, even the bears will listen," he said. He also told Le Gris it was important for the Miamis to speak for the rights to their lands, so that such claims would be recognized in any agreements.

Le Gris remained quiet. He then shook his head.

"If we can draw the fox to our villages, we can take back the places of our ancestors. We can draw their blood to give strength to our fields."

The Turtle answered that the Indians did not have the guns and powder, and could no longer get them from the British. He also said some of the other tribes had already gone to Wayne at Fort Greeneville.

Le Gris said: "If they all agree, I will not agree. If I sign it will mean nothing, because it will mean nothing to the enemy. Only when they fear this can we stand above the land." He lifted an ancient warclub in his bony fingers.

The days passed with little more talk. The Turtle stayed on for the hunt and similar basic pursuits of winter survival in the wilderness. Shortly, other visitors arrived.

"Are you going to rot here in the snow while the mice run to the cat at Fort Greeneville," asked the tall, heavily-jeweled woman.

Tacumwa, sister of Little Turtle, was not a retiring bashful squaw. She was the western half of the most profitable trading business between Quebec and New Orleans. Her husband, Joseph Drouet de Richardville, whom she hadn't seen in some years, operated out of Trois-Rivieres, Canada, far to the east on the St. Lawrence.

Both husband and wife were fond of the distance. They had, however, one strong common passion -- money.

"What do you want me to do, join the mice or go fight the Americans with bows and arrows," said the Turtle, more in derisive statement than a question.

Tacumwa and her son, Jean Baptiste Richardville, sat fingering their wine glasses. They looked across an unpolished walnut table at the Turtle. Both avoided the eyes of Le Gris, who was slouched near the fireplace in the hut.

Bracelets on her arm rattled as she leaned onto the table. "Find out what we can get. You might talk with Charles Beaubien, my dear friend. He has some notions on our taking back what is ours."

"Yes, he can howl as the wolf when it is others who are in reach of the bear's claw." Little Turtle did not object to Beaubien because of his relationship with his sister, both business and otherwise. Marriage, particularly among the chiefs, was a rather casual thing among the Miamis. Though Little Turtle had one wife, Le Gris had four. Though Tacumwa was called Madame de Richardville, she was considered married to Beaubien, located at Miamitown.

But the Turtle had for many years been wary of the self-serving suggestions of Beaubien and other French traders. The warpaths were bloody with the bodies of warriors who found out too late that the cause of battle was some Frenchman or Englishman's trade advantage.

Tacumwa knew she had a problem. Without the help of the Turtle, more months would be lost. She also had to be careful of Le Gris. She feared the old chief of Kekionga who "doesn't think like other people."

The key post in her trading and portage business, Miamitown, was in the hands of the Americans. Since the previous summer, her operations between Detroit and Vincennes had been rubbed out -- first by Wayne's army on the Maumee and now by the new garrison of Fort Wayne.

She did not tell the Turtle she had already been in contact with the agents of the Americans. She asked, however, if the Miami warchief would be willing to go to the fort and talk to the "general" to see if some arrangement could be made. She meant Colonel John Hamtramck at Fort Wayne.

As she expected, the Turtle said he would not deal with the soldiers at the fort at Miamitown, or anywhere else, until all the Indians were in agreement.

"Then perhaps my son can go. Surely that can do no

134

harm."

The Turtle looked at Tacumwa, then at Richardville. He nodded.

As Tacumwa and young Richardville rose to leave, there was a stir over by the fire. "I come with you," said old Le Gris.

Le Gris, Richardville and several other chiefs, together with a party of braves, arrived at the three rivers the following day, Jan. 13, 1795. They led horses along Indian Creek, now called Spy Run Creek, and went across the frozen St. Mary's River. The rubble of the villages was now covered with snow and only an occasional black timber protruded. Even the traders' hovels on the south bank were burned out, excepting one or two stone fireplace walls and chimney.

Though the Americans had been sending agents to talk the Indians into coming to the fort for "treaty talk" for many weeks, they were not especially keen on welcoming the large party of Miamis. Several shots were fired, and a sentry on the garrison wall yelled for the Indians to stay near the river bank.

In a few minutes, Colonel Hamtramck appeared on the wall of the stockade, near the gate which remained closed. He told them several of the Indians could come closer -- up to the fort.

Richardville told the commander the Indians wanted to trade furs and start moving materials down the Maumee to the east and over the portage to the west. "The Americans will then be safe to go down the Wabash," he said.

But Hamtramck was wary. He told Richardville the Indians would have to go to Greeneville to see General Wayne.

Le Gris, enveloped in a buffalo hide, moved in a little closer. He told Hamtramck that Wayne was too far away from the homes of the Indians, and that they could not travel that distance. He said the Indians would meet for treaty talks at Fort Wayne. He also said he would look more favorably at the Americans if the Indians could move back and set up villages at Kekionga.

Hamtramck said the Indians would have to go to Greeneville for parleying with Wayne. Studying the Indians for a moment, he said they could rebuild the village on the other side of the river from the fort. Hamtramck did not open the gates.

Little Turtle watched the odd group trudging up the hill from the St. Joseph River, several miles upstream from the American garrison of Fort Wayne.

There was Tacumwa, his trim erect sister now jangling with jewelry and wrapped in a fur cape; her son, Jean Baptiste, who didn't dress like the Indians any more, and Le Gris, shuffling along through the snow. With them were three warriors who were casually carrying poles with ends decorated with scalps -- taken on New Year's Eve from three deserters from the stockade.

"Jean Baptiste should go to Greeneville today," Tacumwa said as soon as she was within hearing distance. She approached the Miami warchief at an old trader's shack, approximately where the Eero Saarinen-designed Concordia College campus is now located.

The Turtle had decided to let his sister get what she wanted. With care, there would be little lost. There might be an advantage. "Take the greetings of the chiefs of the Miamis to the Black Snake," he said to Richardville. "Speak of our wish that all should meet here at Miamitown where the hatchets were first raised."

The Turtle told his half-breed nephew to promise nothing to Wayne regarding a treaty with the Indian nations. "Your ears will be open to mark down any chiefs who have gone crawling to the enemy with their heads in their hands. We will wait to hear about that when you return."

Tacumwa glanced furtively toward Le Gris and then turned toward the Turtle. "We will want him to speak of the portage."

"What belongs to the Miamis is ours," said the Turtle. "Tell the general we all live here in peace, and our people need the river paths."

Richardville and the warriors started to leave for the fort, where they would meet with a soldier escort for the trip to see General Wayne at Fort Greeneville, some 90

136

miles to the southeast.

"It would be wiser to leave the trophies here," called the Turtle to the warriors, pointing to the poles and scalps. The braves looked at each other and grinned. They tossed the poles against the side of the hut, then hurried on their way.

Among the items carried by the escort officer to Greeneville was a message from John Hamtramck to Anthony Wayne. It said:

"A number of chiefs and warriors of the Miamis arrived at the garrison on the 13th. Having informed them that I could do nothing for them, and that it was necessary for them to proceed to headquarters, finding it inconvenient for so many to go, they selected five, who are under the charge of Lieutenant Massie, and perhaps accompanied by some warriors. The one whose name is Jean Baptiste Richardville is half white and village chief of the nation.

"I shall not say much upon it, except to observe that all the French traders, who were so many machines to the British agents, can be bought. I have had a talk with the chiefs. I have shown them the necessity of withdrawing themselves from the headquarters of corruption, and invited them to come and take possession of their former habitations (across the Maumee and St. Mary's from Fort Wayne) which they have promised me to do.

"Richardville tells me, that as soon as he returns he will go on the Salamonie River on the head of the Wabash and there make a village. He has also promised me to open the navigation of the Wabash to the flag of the United States."

When Richardville arrived at Fort Greeneville, he arranged to meet with General Wayne that evening. He then cast an inquiring eye around the place. He found it in a turmoil of idle soldiers, Kentucky supply operations, Indians who were beginning the habit of seeking handouts, women of the type who attach themselves to such instant communities, and an assortment of backwoods characters. Everyone seemed heavily armed.

Soon he came across William Wells, who was in the company of Simon Kenton, an old frontier scout who

137

headed Wayne's spy operation. Both Richardville and Wells were in their middle 20s. Also, they were relatives of a sort. Richardville was a nephew of Little Turtle. Wells was an adopted son and husband of Little Turtle's daughter. The similarities ended there.

Their dislike for each other showed through the smiles as they exchanged greetings near an outside wall of the stockade. Wells, cocky and the obvious opportunist, was wearing a captain's uniform of the federal army. He had the self-confidence of the man who knows he is on the winning side and will be rewarded for his good judgement.

Richardville continued to smile blandly. He possessed his mother's calculating nature. He was already shuffling mental cards which would one day lead him to wealth beyond the imagination of Wells. Tall and thin, he did not have the other man's bright good looks. But he did have good eyes and ears. He soon learned that Wells had taken up with a young woman from Kentucky.

Jean Baptiste rather enjoyed the role of emissary of the Miami chiefs to the headquarters of Mad Anthony Wayne.

He was struck by the rough simplicity of the American commander's quarters at the stockade. In way of contrast, he remembered his several trips to the places of the British commandants at Detroit and Quebec. There was none of the plush luxury of the Canadian suites here.

As the first emissary of the great Little Turtle, he was treated with special curiosity by the hangers-on at the fort.

Such consideration stopped, however, at Wayne's outer office, where the general's aide, Captain Edward Butler, took a surly attitude. Richardville immediately recognized the younger brother of the hated General Richard Butler, whom the Miamis had killed at the St. Clair defeat. Young Richardville gave no indication that he knew the other man, and acted indifferent to the intended discourtesies. A slight smile played on his face, in fact, when it occurred to him that he could have, if he had thought of it, brought the dead Butler's scalp with him and tossed it into his brother's lap.

Soon, he was shown into Wayne's sanctum. It was a small, rather dimly-lighted room with the usual smell of unaged oak.

The young Miami-Frenchman was astounded to see the great Wayne. The general was in no respect the huge image of invincibility he had expected. He was fairly short, thick in the middle, and tired looking. Richardville was particularly struck by the almost green palor of Wayne's face.

However, Wayne stood to greet him with a sure good manner; and his uniform was of a correctness that was unusual in the frontier area. Wayne quickly engaged in pleasantries, but Richardville was astute enough to notice that each inquiry was at least partially designed to gain information on the disposition of the Indians.

The conversation turned to the proposed treaty. "We have had the pleasure of visits from the chiefs of many of the Indian nations," Wayne said. "I ask you now; when can we receive our brothers of the Miamis -- your Little Turtle, Le Gris and Pacan."

Richardville, thinking to gain the identities of earlier Indian visitors, said: "Perhaps the chiefs you speak of only talk for the dogs and rabbits."

Wayne was not tempted. "The chiefs are leaders of their people," he said bluntly. "I will come to peaceful terms with them, and they are willing to accept the fatherly hand of the United States. The tribes of those chiefs who will not sit in council with us will have only themselves to blame for their loss and suffering."

Richardville changed the vein. "The great warchief of the Miami Nation, Little Turtle, sends to you his greetings in a spirit of peace. He says all the leaders of the Indians can come together if the council fires are kindled at Miamitown, where you have already built a strong fortress. Let us bury the hatchet where it was first raised."

Wayne looked evenly at Richardville. "Yes, there the hatchet was first raised. Those are harsh grounds of war. We have had enough of that. There are no bloody traces here. We shall have the treaty council here."

The American general had already weighed the possibility of a place of council along the Maumee, and had decided against it. There was the difficulty of supply and the dangers of renewed warfare so far into the Indian country. The Crane, a Wyandot chief, had told Wayne of

139

Le Gris and his plan for tricking the Americans. "The red men will make the meetings last as long as they can," the Indian had said, "and when the food and supplies of the white men run out, they will attack the fort." In a letter to the War Department, Wayne spoke of his refusal to have treaty negotiations at Kekionga. "Should they prove treacherous, we should be placed in an unpleasant position," Wayne wrote.

Richardville switched subjects again. "There is the matter of the portage." He told Wayne that the reopening of the water route from the Great Lakes to the Mississippi by the Maumee-Wabash land link would "enrich the Americans." He asked Wayne to instruct the Fort Wayne garrison to allow the Miamis to use the portage, with Tacumwa and himself as "directoires d'affaires." Richardville also hinted that Wayne might want to be a partner in the portage profits.

Wayne told Richardville the question of use of the waterways in the Northwest would be settled at the Treaty Council.

Three days travel time to the northwest, Little Turtle sat quietly looking into the fire as Richardville told of his talks with General Wayne at Fort Greeneville.

"What did you sign," the Turtle asked suddenly, without moving his eyes from the flickering flames.

"Nothing. Nothing of importance," said the nephew. Richardville explained that he had only agreed that the Miamis would attend talks the following June at Greeneville. He said the chiefs of the Chippewas, Potawatomis and Sacs had also told Wayne they would participate in the parley. Nothing had been conceded, he said.

Richardville then told the Miami warchief that Wayne would take up the matter of the Maumee-Wabash portage at the council fire.

"The Crane is already in the Black Snake's pouch," Richardville said. "Many of the Wyandots are at the general's gate, waiting for him to scatter daily rations of grain. Some of the Delawares are also standing by his door."

The Turtle said the hunger of the Indians was one of the weaknesses of the many tribes that winter. Even the Miamis, some of them, were seeking handouts from the American garrison at Fort Wayne.

Little Turtle opened the palm of his hand, extending it toward Richardville. He traced his finger in a series of lines across it and listed the difficulties of bringing all the Indian nations into a single voice for negotiations with the United States.

"I have here the Weas, the Kaskaskias, the Mingos, the Kickapoos, the Potawatomis, the Chippewas, the Ottawas and the Sacs. They will be with us as one voice. But the Wyandots are lost to the enemy. The Delawares are like nervous squaws, changing with the clouds.

"Blue Jacket of the Shawnees will be with us. Tecumseh and some of the young men of the Shawnees will not sit in council with the Americans. We must talk with Le Gris again," said the Turtle.

But as the snows gave way to the spring thaw, Little Turtle found much of the strength of the Indians was likewise melting away. There was hunger and bickering. There was envy and secret maneuverings. The British made it clear that their new policy precluded any possibility of their supplying the Indians in any new war campaigns. Lord Dorchester, governor-general of Canada, got word to Little Turtle that it would be wiser to sit down with the Americans and seek the best terms he could get.

Colonel Hamtramck at Fort Wayne was elated with what he considered a coup in March of that year, 1795. He wrote to Wayne:

"Le Gris, the village chief of the Miami nation, and one of the commanding trumps of McKee's game, has at last come in. He stood out for a long time.

"I have promised him a great deal of butter with his bread, but your excellency very well knows that flies are not caught with gall and bitter. He was four days with me, during which time I had the opportunity of examining him

141

with great attention.

"He is a sensible old fellow, and in no ways ignorant of the cause of the war, for which he blames the Americans, saying they were too extravagant in their demands in their first treaties; that the country they claimed by virtue of the definitive treaty of 1783 was preposterous; that the King of Great Britain never had claimed their land after the conquest of Canada, and far less ever attempted to take any part of it without the consent of the aborigines, and of consequence, had no authority to cede their country to the United States."

Le Gris walked slowly from the fort, down to the foot of the river. After a few minutes, he turned and looked back at the stockade. He then turned again and crossed the Maumee to the north bank area where some of the Miamis were building huts at the old village site.

A squaw, wailing in a steady drone, was holding a sick child. There was the smell of fires for the noon meal, but there was little to eat. Few of the men were to be seen. Two growling mongrels were pulling at some grey substance, but moved away as Le Gris went by.

The old chief was not satisfied with the American. He had observed Hamtramck carefully. The officer had listened politely enough when Le Gris told him the Indians would hold to their ancestorial lands. But Le Gris could tell by the look of the man's eyes that when he nodded he was really saying nothing. It would always be that way. They would nod their heads, but then take whatever was within their power to take.

He drew the old buffalo hide closer around his shoulders and went slowly for a mile or so north along the river bank. He turn turned again and looked back to the three rivers with the fort beyond. The scattering of huts on the near side reminded him of the twig houses children made with the river mud, and just about as temporary. There was a chill he could feel in the northwest wind.

When Little Turtle and Le Gris and a party of Miamis arrived at Fort Greeneville the following June 23, they found the place a crowd of activity and bad odors.

The Miamis were among the last to arrive. More than 1,000 Indians of the many tribes were already on the scene -- some for several weeks. Noise, fires and smoky wigwams created, at least on this occasion, an unpleasant atmosphere. The Turtle remembered, in contrast, the almost magic quality of the great councils of war in the days of the Miami victories.

But losers are poor company. Intrigues, knifings and brawling occupied the time of many of the warriors as the days passed. Adding to the discontent were reports of unsavory actions in the Indian country -- groups driven by greed and revenge were crossing the Ohio and striking some Indian villages.

Wayne was particularly incensed because these premature grabs threatened to undo his settlement with the various tribes. One of the bloody gangs was headed by Parson Findlay, whom Wayne charged with "sinful aggression by his guilty horde of plunderers."

The Turtle stood mostly aloof from the talks with the Americans during the early council period. He and Le Gris had come to Greeneville mainly to protect the Indians from making foolish agreements and to hold up the interests of the Miamis.

But it soon became apparent that some of the chiefs were willing to agree to most any terms suggested by Wayne. The American general proposed the Indians agree to the terms of the Treaty of Fort Harmar, which would take most of the area of the present state of Ohio and a number of key sites in Indiana, Michigan and Illinois from the Indians.

At this point, Little Turtle stood up and walked to the center of the meeting place.

"I expect that the land on the Wabash and in this country belongs to me and my people. I now take the opportunity to inform my brethren of the United States and others present that there are men of sense and understanding among my people as well as theirs, and these lands were disposed of without our knowledge or consent."

He swung his right arm around toward Wayne. "You have pointed out the boundary line between the Indian lands and the United States, but I now take the liberty to inform you that the line cuts off from the Indians a large portion of country which as been enjoyed by my forefathers from time immemorial without molestation or dispute.

"The prints of my ancestors' houses are everywhere to be seen in this portion. I was a little astonished at hearing you and my brethren present, telling each other what business you had transacted at Muskingum concerning this country.

"It is well known that my forefathers kindled the first fire at Detroit; from thence he extended his lines to the headwaters of the Scioto; from thence to the mouth; from thence down along the Ohio to the mouth of the Wabash and thence to Lake Michigan.

"I have now informed you of the boundaries of the Miami nation where the Great Spirit placed by forefathers a long time ago, charging them not to sell or part with his lands, but to preserve them for his posterity."

The Turtle, in effect, was repudiating Wayne and his terms for a peace settlement. Wayne didn't then know, as Little Turtle did, that the Miamis had been on most of the land in question for less than 100 years. The French explorer, La Salle, and others had urged the Miamis to move east as a buffer between the Iroquois and Great Lakes area trading routes. The Miamis had muscled out some other tribes. The area included western Ohio, all of Indiana, the southern part of Michigan and the portion of Illinois near Lake Michigan.

The American general did not answer the Miami warchief immediately. He waited two days, during which time he learned from some other tribal leaders that many Indians opposed the Miami land control.

"I have paid attention to what Little Turtle said two days since, concerning the land he claims," Wayne said on July 24.

"These boundaries enclose a very large space of country, indeed they embrace, if I mistake not, all the lands on which all the nations present now live, as well as those which have been ceded to the United States. Then Little Turtle says, the prints of his forefathers' houses are everywhere to be seen within these boundaries," Wayne told the council.

The general looked toward Little Turtle, saying: "It is true these prints are observed, but at the same time we discover the marks of the French possessions throughout this country." He mentioned Detroit, Vincennes, Ouiatenon (Lafayette), Chicago, St. Joseph, Mich., and both French and British marks at Fort Wayne and the Maumee area. Mad Anthony Wayne, sensing the deepness of the disagreement among the Indians, pushed for a complete capitulation to American terms.

Actually, Wayne went beyond his instructions from the War Department. The thinking back east was that Wayne should relinquish some claims along the Maumee and Wabash rather than risk a renewal of the mostly disasterous wars in the Old Northwest.

But in the steamy summer night of the Ohio wilderness, the general saw that he could secure the entire area below the Great Lakes in one bold stroke. The decision, which was to prove successful, would set the course for American expansion in the entire West. Had the British been able to hold parts of the Great Lakes area, the U. S. movement beyond the Mississippi would have been far more limited in the years to follow.

On that same humid night in late July, less than a quarter mile from Wayne's quarters inside Fort Greeneville, sat Little Turtle and Le Gris.

"Pork and whisky is what they want," said the old Miami chief to the Turtle. Le Gris held up a jug, took a swig, then threw it at a Delaware chief who happened to be nearby.

Both the Turtle and Le Gris knew that most of the tribal chiefs had already given in to the demands of Anthony Wayne. Nothing short of a war between the Indian factions would break the agreements, and the Miami chiefs decided that would be suicidal. Even at that, the Wyandot Chief Crane was protected day and night because it was whispered that Le Gris was weaving designs to cut him down.

The next morning, Little Turtle arose to stir the Indians

145

one last time. He turned his back to General Wayne and his staff and faced the assembled Indians.

"Listen, you chiefs and warriors, to what I am about to say to you. To you I am speaking."

Pointing to Anthony Wayne, the Miami warchief said "Our elder brother says we gave some lands of our forefathers to the French and British. I expected to have him deliver those words." The Turtle then warned against any fast agreement to the American terms. "I hope we will take time to consider the subject, that we will unite in an opinion and express it unanimously."

Turning to Wayne, the Turtle said neither the French nor the British "told us they wished to purchase these lands from us." He said the place "where your fort now stands" at Miamitown "was always ours."

"The next place you pointed to was the Little River, and you said you wanted two square miles at that place. It was always ours. This carrying place has provided subsistance to your younger brothers." Taking a conciliatory tack, the Turtle suggested "Let us both own this place and enjoy in common the advantages it affords." The Turtle understood the sensitivity of the portage. The group which controlled it held the upper hand in the river traffic between the Great Lakes and the Mississippi, and the strategic advantage in that era.

Wayne gave a fast reply, and appealed to the discontent of the other Indians. "I find there is some objections to the reservation at Fort Wayne. The Little Turtle observes he never heard of any cessions made at that place to the French.

"I have traced two forts at that point; one stood at the junction of the St. Joseph with the St. Mary's, and the other not far removed on the St. Mary's. It has been the established rule among Europeans to reserve as much ground around their forts as their cannon can command."

The Turtle was not given the opportunity at this point to remind the Americans that the Indians had sacked and burned the first fort along the St. Mary's, and had later taken the second fort from its British garrison by subterfuge. Both had been built by the French, but the Europeans had been unable to hold either of them against the Miamis. Wayne continued his argument:

"Objection has also been made respecting the portage between Fort Wayne and Little River, that the road had been to the Miamis a source of wealth, and produced them one hundred dollars a day. But who in fact paid this heavy contribution. It is true the traders bore it in the first instance, but they laid it on the Indians of the Wabash. It is the Little Beaver, the Soldier, the Sun and their tribes who have actually been so highly taxed." He told the other Indians that they would no longer have to pay the Miamis for use of the portage.

Little Turtle and Le Gris looked with distaste as most of the tribal leaders grunted approval of Wayne's words. Generally, there seemed to be a perverse pleasure in seeing the former warchief of the great confederacy being put down.

A few days later, Wayne attempted to placate the Miami chiefs by reducing slightly some of the land areas being taken in the treaty. He kept the federal hand, however, on the key military tracts and the entire Ohio country except the northwest quarter. It was agreed that all prisoners and hostages would be exchanged.

Little Turtle and Le Gris signed the treaty. They hoped a clear-cut agreement between the U. S. and all the tribes would at least give the Indians a permanent country. Besides, there was small choice under the circumstances on that day of August 3, 1795.

In this single treaty, the Indians signed away the sites of the future cities of Detroit, Toledo, Fort Wayne, South Bend, Lafayette, Vincennes, Chicago and Peoria, all in tracts in the Indian country, plus the Ohio area which today contains Cleveland, Columbus, Dayton, Cincinnati, Akron and most of the other populated centers.

With the Treaty of Greeneville, the era of war ended and the era of schemes and land grabs began.

Thus, the pattern of American expansion across a continent, from the Allegheny Mountains to the Pacific Coast, was irreversibly set. Never again would the natives on the land, the Indians, interrupt or materially change this westward ho. There would be skirmishes and new treaties, deathly raids and broken agreements, but never a real hesitation in a migration which was to be continuous for 100 years.

Even before Little Turtle left Miamitown in the summer of 1796 to meet Anthony Wayne at Detroit, many of the Indians were already on the move. This was happening while further to the east the American pioneers were rushing across the Ohio River for the new "safe" lands so recently taken from "the savages."

First to move from the Miami lands were bands of Delawares who were encouraged by Spanish governors along the Mississippi. It was thought that the Indians would be useful soldiers to protect kingdoms which were being established in the wilderness. There were several schemes to set up independent holdings in the wide disorganized frontier area.

French groups were renewing efforts to form settlements. British interests still sought to retain trade advantages and political influence in places where their activities would be relatively unobtrusive. Even some of the settlers in Kentucky were drawn to these mostly imaginary plans for wilderness nations. General Wilkinson, left by Wayne in charge of the American Army at Greeneville, was approached, and later suspected of seditious dealings with the aim of putting together a kingdom along the Mississippi.

The Turtle and Blue Jacket, the Shawnee chief, were already at Fort Detroit when General Wayne arrived on August 13, 1796. Wayne, who had returned home to Pennsylvania for several months, sailed in a sloop across Lake Erie and up the Detroit River. He came to supervise a transfer of power: the taking over of Fort Detroit from the British forces, as provided by the Jay Treaty between the United States and Great Britain.

Many Indians were on hand for the proceedings, though they really had no hand in them. The Turtle stood at the landing place as Wayne came down a catwalk. He noticed that the general could hardly make his own way, and had to be helped ashore.

Some time later, after the drums of British and

American corps gave due notice of the outgoing British garrison and the incoming Americans, the Miami warchief made his way to Wayne's quarters. This was no novelty to the Turtle. He was far more familiar with forts at Detroit and the surroundings than was Anthony Wayne. He had visited commanders there who were French, British and now American.

"I hope you will find yourself as welcome here now as in the past," Wayne said with the suggestion of a smile.

After the greeting was translated, the Turtle replied in French. "The many nations look for peace and a more permanent friendship with you than was experienced with those who were here before." He then spoke of the building of new trading posts in the Indian country and use of the riverways by both the Indians and the Americans. "Our people now look to the United States to exchange the gifts of the forest for the things they need." Little Turtle would for some time yet be under the illusion that the Indians could build their own self-supporting communities along side those of the Americans.

The Miami chief asked Wayne, when he returned to the eastern cities, if he would speak to "Those teachers who can show our people the ways" of the organized societies.

Little Turtle didn't know it at the moment, but it was he and not Wayne who would soon be in the capital cities of the U. S. Before leaving the fort, he had the conviction that Wayne was a broken man in every way except a strain of iron will.

Mad Anthony Wayne, at 51, was at the end of the line. He was at odds with his family, because of outside love affairs and rounds of heavy-drinking night life. His health was broken for the same reasons and because of the strenuous campaigning. He was disappointed career wise when the cabinet post of Secretary of War went to another who was less able but had better political connections. He was plagued by damaging whisper campaigns, largely untrue, spread by political enemies including General Wilkinson.

Wayne set sail for Pennsylvania in November. When only part way across Lake Erie, it became obvious he was a dying man. He was taken off the ship at Presque Isle near the south shore. Eaten with gout and gangrene, he

149

was in a state of agony. One of his legs swelled to twice its normal size. Lying in a make-shift cabin in the fort, he wished for death but lingered for three weeks. It was there that Mad Anthony Wayne died on Dec. 15, 1796.

Chapter 13

By the time of the Treaty of Fort Wayne in June, 1803, Little Turtle's dreams for an Indian culture within the folds of American expansion were already badly shaken.

In the first days following the end of the war period, there had been heady possibilities. Chief Little Turtle, together with William Wells, went to the American Capitol at Philadelphia. There he became an immediate celebrity. He was received by President Washington and Cabinet members. People pointed to him on the streets as "the great chief who defeated the armies of General Harmar and General St. Clair." He was awarded gifts and momentos by the heros of the Revolution, such as Kosciusko and Von Steuben. Gilbert Stuart painted his portrait, which later went up in flames when the British burned the White House in the War of 1812.

On that first trip, and later visits to Baltimore and other cities, the Turtle pushed for plans which would, if hoped, make the Indians self-sufficient. In addition to Washington, he talked with both President Adams and President Jefferson along these lines. Thomas Jefferson showed particular interest. The Turtle, whose family was loosely Catholic because of its French ties, approached the Quakers about sending teachers to the Indian country, which they agreed to do.

But as time went on, everything the Turtle touched seemed to slowly decay and turn to dust. He traded off some Indian lands in exchange for farming tools and funds to start the Indians in new methods and products of agriculture. But slick traders soon gave whisky to the Indians for the equipment.

Government money to the tribes usually went the same way. Blue Jacket bought large stocks of whisky and whole villages of Shawnees, men and women alike, went on drunken sprees. Instead of supporting Indian independence, the government handouts broke any

151

resourcefulness the Indians had, as they took on an attitude of dependence which became permanent.

The Quakers came to teach the Indians, but few of the tribesmen were any longer interested. It came to nothing. Eventually, the main preoccupation of the Quakers seemed to be bickering with Wells, who had been named Indian agent. The Quakers told Territorial Governor William Henry Harrison, appointed to that post when the territory was formed on July 4, 1800, that Wells was converting money intended for the Indians to his own use. The Quakers went back to Baltimore.

Little Turtle noticed, however, that not all the Indians were doing so badly. A few were thriving, and these happened to be his relatives.

His sister Tecumwa and her son Jean Baptiste Richardville were busy. Their instincts led them into quite a few profitable situations. Each time land concessions were made, their own holdings seemed to grow. To this day, their names appear on old abstracts covering tracts over wide areas of territory. They worked between the lines of the trade regulations until the river and portage traffic was largely their thing. It was said that Richardville, who eventually became one of the nation's richest men, helped fund the fur trade of one Jakob Waldorf who changed his name to John Jacob Astor.

Chiefs of the other Indian tribes noticed Little Turtle's special relationship with the American Administration and the success of the family operations. They set up a howl.

"It is a great misfortune that the neighboring Indians are so extremely jealous of Little Turtle who really appears to be a man of extraordinary talents," wrote Secretary of War Henry Dearborn to Harrison in 1802. "It is the intention of the President to use every means to introduce husbandry and domestic manufacturing among the Indians." He also reported "complaints of white plunderers" and told Harrison to "prohibit the sale of spirits."

But President Jefferson proceeded with his intention of getting the land from the Indians, a necessary part of his ambition for an expansion westward of the United States.

152

Gradually, his main pawn in this became Little Turtle.

"The President desires you to suspend leasing of Salt Springs and sound the Indians on the subject of ceding the spring and adjacent land to the U.S.," Dearborn told Harrison. "It is presumed that the Little Turtle and Mr. Wells may be employed on such a mission to advantage. There is reason to believe the Turtle will have considerable influence with those nations -- the Potawatomis and the Kickapoos."

The following year President Jefferson told Secretary Dearborn to be sure to include the Turtle on a mission which would have far greater impact on the future growth of the nation. It was to prepare the way for the founding of Fort Dearborn at the old Miami village of Chikago, and lead to the eventual metropolis of Chicago.

The instructions of May 26, 1803, were sent by the Secretary of War to William Wells at Fort Wayne:

"As we are about to establish a military post at Chikago on the land ceded to the United States, it will be necessary for the purpose of keeping up a communication between that post and Fort Wayne, to have a direct path or bridle road from one post to the other as the nature of the country will admit.

"You will therefore please to take the earliest opportunity of looking out and designating such a track or path, and you will report your proceeding there to this office, with the opinion of the distance, and whether the natives will have any objections to our improving such a communication for the express and driving of cattle."

Dearborn also told Wells, who was Federal Indian Agent at that time for all the tribes in the Northwest Territory, to "ascertain how far the river St. Joseph (from South Bend) is navigible for boats" and "whether there are any other white inhabitants on the St. Joseph or near Chikago. I should wish to have the Little Turtle go with you if he has no objections."

Wells and Little Turtle set out immediately with a party. They followed an old Indian trail which soon became known as the Dearborn Road. This wilderness trail took

153

them to the river at South Bend. They also charted north of South Bend a route long called the Dragoon Trail, so-named because of the soldiers who for years after traveled through the vicinity in going to and from Fort Dearborn and Fort Wayne. The Dragoon Trail still exists today as a walking path across the north campus of the University of Notre Dame.

The inclusion of the Miami warchief in the action was a stroke of genius. Little Turtle was still at that time determined on good relations with the United States. He saw cooperation as a route for the Indians to become a regular part of the American community. But of more immediate importance, the Chikago site had been at one time a recognized part of the Miami country. Though the Potawatomies had become dominent in the vicinity, they respected the spirit of the ancestors of the Miamis who still hovered over the shores of Lake Michigan.

When the Turtle came upon the site that summer of 1803, he quietly sat down with several Potawatomi chiefs and possibly one or two Winnebagoes, whom the Potawatomies were permitting to settle some distance away. The sachems then walked about the scene, parleying and pointing out the land which had been taken by the U. S. in the Treaty of Greeneville in 1795.

Whether the Miami chief encountered any strong arguments against the fort is not known. But in the coming months, the other Indians would accept the building of the stockade without resistance.

Standing near the shoreline, as the breeze off the lake stirred the sand around them, Little Turtle marked two lines on the ground. He pulled the long barrel of a dueling pistol along the sand as the other chiefs watched. The place was just south of the Chikago village river, near where it flowed into Lake Michigan.

Whether by previous plan or because of Little Turtle's marks, Major John Whistler began construction of the ill-fated fort several weeks later at that exact same spot.

Barking dogs and the sounds of horse hooves alerted the drowsy Miami chief on a hot afternoon in 1805.

154

Coming into Little Turtle's village at Devil's Lake was a group of mounted soldiers from Fort Wayne. As they approached, the Turtle noticed that one of the men was holding a packet. He also noticed, as the soldier approached, that he had a forced and questioning smile on his face.

The Miami chief took the packet, which was addressed from Thomas Jefferson, the President of the United States, to The Little Turtle, Chief of the Miami Indian Nations. In the note, Jefferson complimented the Turtle for helping the cause of peace and thanked him for his part in settling several land disputes in the Indian country.

From the moment the letter arrived at the fort, it had grated on the men of the garrison. "Private correspondence from the President of the United States to this bloody savage," was a typical remark. Many of the soldiers were long-suffering frontier rustics with ingrained fear, hatred and contempt for any Indian. It was particularly galling that it was President Jefferson, the most exalted of all to the common man, who wrote the note.

Later, with further exchanges of notes between Jefferson and the Turtle, it became almost too much to bear. The fort commander, thinking to tip off General Harrison about these direct "approaches" between Indian and President, sent a message dated Feb. 28, 1806, complaining about such contact "around" the territorial governor.

But Harrison was previously aware of the relationship and encouraged it. Millions of acres of land were being purchased from the Indians. These agreements were opening up vast areas of what is now Ohio, Indiana, Michigan, Illinois and Wisconsin to settlement. Migration was so fast that Ohio was admitted to the Union in 1803. Still having his run of bad luck, Governor Arthur St. Clair advised against Ohio statehood, but was unanimously voted down. Jefferson removed him soon after.

The Michigan Territory was organized by Congress on Jan. 11, 1805. Prior to that, Michigan and part of Northern Indiana had been known as Wayne County of the Indiana Territory. Illinois, which previously had been a part of Indiana, was organized as a separate territory on Feb. 3,

1809.

Some of the treaties had the aura of a successful confidence game at the Indians' expense. Harrison wrote to Jefferson on Aug. 27, 1805: "I do myself the honor to enclose the treaty" and said the price of about one cent per acre was "higher than I would have hoped."

"I pursued your directions relative to the Turtle. You will receive from him a letter expressing his great satisfaction at the result of the conference and his devotion to the United Státes," said Harrison.

Some of the other chiefs weren't so satisfied. They complained and occasionally became threatening. The usual method was to buy them off. Secretary of War Dearborn told Harrison: "Should you judge it advantageous to distribute two or three hundred dollars among the Miamis, Potawatomis and others, by way of quieting their minds in the relation to the sale of lands by the Delawares and Piankashaws, you will do it."

Later, Wells told the Secretary of War that Marpac, the Potawatomi warchief, was a source of trouble, but his friendship could be bought for $800.

Soon, however, Little Turtle found himself in the middle of more serious problems. He told Wells to warn the Americans about The Prophet, the brother of Tecumseh, who was "collecting the Indians at Greeneville and has runners out in all directions, expecting 2,000 Indians within a month." He also said the best way to settle things would be to "get rid of The Prophet."

The Turtle disliked The Prophet for two reasons. First, he considered the Shawnee medicine man to be insane, probably with good reasons. Also, due to the heavy influx of settlers, he saw hostilities with the Americans not only suicidal, but pointless.

But The Prophet kept beating the drums for war. He and his brother, Tecumseh, moved to a location near the Wabash along the Tippecanoe River and founded Prophetstown.

In the early spring The Turtle and other chiefs went down the Wabash River to dislodge the growing band of The Prophet. Wells noted at the time: "The Little Turtle has just come from seeing the Shawnee Prophet 60 miles

156

southwest of Fort Wayne. They were in council 10 days ..
but the Prophet is determined to gather Indians to start
war on the other Indians and white people. The Turtle and
nine other chiefs wanted to forbid the Prophet from settling on the Wabash." But The Prophet stayed and the
Turtle couldn't do anything about it.

It was early in 1810 when Little Turtle noticed the first
sure sign of war clouds in the Indian country. British rifles
were beginning to appear in some of the villages.

But in the misty decade before some semblance of order
was brought to the wilderness area, the real causes for
hostile action went deeper than firearms. There was the
loss of the old way of life. There was loss of the Indian
lands, truly thought of as hunting grounds by most Indians,
rather than an individual sense of property ownership.
And there was the firewater.

The Prophet was a reformed drunkard. With the zeal of
the dispossessed, the Shawnee claimed he "rose up from
the place of the dead." He was attracting warriors from
the rivers and the lake villages with stories of sorceries
and magical tricks.

At first, he had only limited success. But his stock with
the Indians jumped apace when he made his famous curse,
and made good on it.

Tecumseh, The Prophet's brother, (old stories have it
that they were two parts of a triplet birth) had vowed
death to all chiefs who had signed the Treaty of Fort
Wayne. In that treaty and others, nearly 30 million acres
of Indian lands had been ceded.

The Prophet decided to go one better. In a dramatic
gesture, including various incantations and possibly the
burning of at least two witches, he decreed that the first
chief to die would be Leatherlips of the Wyandots.
Leatherlips and others had participated with Little Turtle
in the land concessions to the Americans. A few days after
the curse was laid on, the doomed chief was found with a
crushed skull. It was likely that Chief Leatherlips was
dispatched by a Wyandot warrior under the Shawnee
chief's influence, but the air of mystery added to The
Prophet's stature.

In the meantime, Tecumseh was calling for the "war dances" and began a series of trips in the upper lakes and to the Mississippi, beating the drums for a new Indian army.

By the following year, hundreds of braves were gathering at The Prophetstown on the lower Tippecanoe. Threats of total destruction of the white race were heard over a wide area. Actual raids, however, were limited to a few isolated incidents, including the firing of shots at a couple of soldiers.

Fear, because of the terrible death tolls of the old days, gripped a thousand miles of frontier. Governor Harrison, headquartered at the territorial capital at Vincennes, decided to take action. He led a force of about 1,000 men up the Wabash for a show of strength.

The American troops, a mixed force of regulars and militia, settled into a camp near the Tippecanoe. The Prophetstown was a short distance away.

Before dawn on Nov. 17, 1811, the Indians made a headlong rush through a cold drizzle at the Americans. The Prophet had told the braves they would sweep through the soldiers but would be immune from injury and death themselves.

It didn't turn out that way. Of the 600 Indians in the attack, some 200 were killed. The others were decisively repulsed. The American losses totaled 60 killed and more than 100 wounded. Tecumseh didn't participate in the Battle of Tippecanoe. He was on the way with additional warriors, but the battle was over and lost before he could get there. This conflict was in no way of the size, sweep or strategy of the days of the Miami Confederacy. It was, however, a highly popular event in the lives of the growing population of the frontier states and states to be. It made a hero of Harrison and furnished him with a successful Presidential campaign slogan.

Little Turtle was disgusted when he heard of the battle and the useless loss of the Indians. He figured the entire episode damaged an already decaying Indian position.

Other things were going to pieces too. His son-in-law, William Wells, had been demoted from Indian agent for the territory to the job of subagent at a post. He had been accused of double dealing by the War Department.

But no one accused Wells, the one-time Kentucky farm boy who was kidnapped by the Indians, of lack of courage. And he was to prove himself in a final action.

As the War of 1812 broke out, nearly 1,100 Indians, mostly Potawatomi, beseiged Fort Dearborn, built near the site of the old Miami village of Chicago (called Chikago at that time). Wells volunteered to lead a party of Miami Indians to aid the garrison. They struck a course from Fort Wayne along the old Dearborn Trail.

When he arrived at the fort, Wells saw that the garrison, which included women and children, had left the stockade in the hope the Indians would allow them to pass through in safety. The Indians, under Chief Blackbird, however, moved in and began to cut up the group, including the children.

Wells organized a defense for the remainder, some of whom survived. But not Wells, whose Miami party had ducked out.

When the Indians saw Wells, they went after him in screaming vengeance. He was cut down by a riddle of rifle balls in the sand dunes along Lake Michigan where downtown Chicago is now located. He was then tomahawked and scalped. His head was cut off and his heart was cut out.

Little Turtle left his wife at his village near Eel River. She was his second wife, and the younger sister of his first wife who had died some years earlier.

She stood there with her hands at her side -- standing in the doorway of the stone and timber house. There was no sound but the summer noises from the pond and woods.

The Turtle had difficulty staying on his horse as he rode toward Fort Wayne. He certainly did not feel or look the part of earlier times. His appearance a half dozen years before was described by E. D. Mansfield, young son of the surveyor general of the U. S. who was located at Cincinnati at the time.

"One day a dark complexioned man with swarthy

countenance, riding a very fine horse, dismounted at our house and went into my father's office. I wanted to go in and see him, but for some reason was not allowed to. After some time I saw him come out and mount his horse and ride rapidly away.

"I asked my mother -- who is that man? She said: That is Little Turtle, the great Miami chief."

But riding now across the countryside, the Turtle was no longer thinking of land surveys, or even the problems of whisky-drinking Indians, several of whom he passed along the way. All his attention was on the foot of his right leg. And with each jolt of the horse, his attention became more acutely focused on that point.

The Miami chief had a case of gout which was in its final stages. Even with his passive and pain-resisting nature, he could no longer carry it off. He was on his way to see a garrison surgeon.

As he plodded along in the heat of the summer sun, he went into a coma of feverish dreams. In his illusions he could see a familiar place, yet changed. Some Indian people were being dragged onto flat scows. Shriveled women and wailing children huddled in them. There were many such boats, all crowded. A voice in the dream said: "These are the children of the Miamis."

Other feverish pictures showed Indian men being chased down by paid hunters. These Indians too were pulled onto the boats. The place was not the river, but a very straight waterway. A crowd of people stood along the banks watching. There was a large sign: "Wabash-Erie Canal Opening: 1843."

In the strange dream, the loaded scows moved east for a distance and then south as far as the Ohio River at Cincinnati. There was hot sun and chill rain on the open boats as the journey continued down the Ohio day after day. At the Father of Rivers, the boats went upstream to the Missouri, then again west on the wide river.

In the Turtle's feverish illusions, he could see days, weeks and months go by, but the journey continued. Finally, there was a wide space, treeless to the horizon. Here the children of the Miamis were forced off the boats as snow swept across the place. The boats disappeared from the image and the Indians were standing alone on the bleak Kansas plains. The image continued but the figures began to slip away in the blizzard. The feverish picture then began to change with the coming of spring and there in the sun were only half the children of the Miami, still slowly moving west.

The vision faded with a start as the Turtle needed all his conscious strength to hold himself on his mount. The animal walked up to and stopped at the stockade gates of Fort Wayne.

After a few minutes, three soldiers came out and took the Indian down from his horse. The army surgeon later said there was nothing to be done for either the leg or the man. He was carried across the St. Mary's River to a shelter on the land of William Wells.

Little Turtle asked that he be laid on a grass mat in the open, where he could see the sky and river. He knew he was dying.

It was quiet those last days. Few people came to see him. He was 60 years old, and to some, he was now known as the Judas goat who led the Indians down the trail toward landless squalor.

Through the history of the American Indians, no other chief would lead so potent a native army to such astonishing victories. Only the Turtle was able to roll back, for a generation, the push by the United States to expand westward.

But that was 20 years before. By now the old warchief had lived too long. He was dying a natural death -- hardly the way of a hero.

No monument would be built to Little Turtle. No stone likeness would be chipped on a mountainside. There would be no streets in downtown Chicago, such as was even named after his son-in-law Wells. No towns were named -- not even cigar store Indian figures, thousands of which were to be called Tecumseh. His name would never become a household word.

It was on July 14, 1812, when Little Turtle last heard human sounds. Two French-speaking traders who were celebrating Bastille Day came by. When they returned a little later, the Turtle was dead.

161

The Miami warchief was not buried by his own people. A group of soldiers from the fort, the one-time enemy, gave him military rites. A number of curious Indians watched, however, as the funeral group with muffled drums walked by. He was carried to a gravesite in an orchard, just west of the St. Joseph River. A grandson, Chief Coesse, read a funeral message.

Relics of better days, including a sword given by George Washington, were buried with the body. Someone retrieved at the last moment, however, a gold watch given by Gen. Haldimand in the high times of old.

As the soldiers turned to leave, a young private asked a sergeant next to him, "Who is that tall strange-looking Indian standing alone over there on the hill?"

"That's old Le Gris. He is chief of all the Miamis now."

The soldier looked back, but the figure was gone.

The End

Notes and Sources

Events and quotations in this book are taken from official documents and diaries of the period where available. Since the Indians left few written records, conversations among them are largely reconstructed in the context of their actions. The author's thanks go to Ernest E. Williams, editor and Helene Foellinger, publisher of The News-Sentinel, for their interest in this volume and the newspaper series which preceded it.

The following bibliography lists the main sources of information:

George Washington, Messages and Papers of the President.
John Adams, Messages and Papers of the President.
Thomas Jefferson, Messages and Papers of the President.
Frederick Haldimand, Governor-General of Canada, Papers in Archives Publique, Ottawa.
Allen County-Fort Wayne Historical Society Publications.
Alvord, Clarence W., The Illinois Country.
Anson, Bert, The Miami Indians.
Bailey, Kenneth P., The Ohio Company of Virginia and Westward Movement.
Barnhart, John D., Valley of Democracy.
Charles H. Bartlett and Richard Lyon, LaSalle and the Valley of the St. Joseph.
Benton, Elbert Jay, Wabash Trade Route.
Boone, Daniel, Memoirs.
Brice, Wallace A., A History of Fort Wayne.
Bussard, H. J., Miami Indian Words.
Cass, Lewis, Notes on Indians on the Old Northwest.
Charlevoix, Pierre F. X., History of New France.
Cooke, Captain John, Diary at Fort Wayne in 1794.
Dawson, John W., Old Times in Fort Wayne.
Dillon, John B., A History of Indiana.
Downes, Randolph C., Council Fire of the Upper Ohio.
Dunn, Jacob Piatt, True Indian Stories.
Dunbar, Willis F., Michigan.
Esarey, Logan, Messages and Letters of William Henry Harrison.
Griswold, Bert J., The Pictorial History of Fort Wayne.
Godfrey, Chief Clarence, Miami Indian Stories.
Hanna, Charles, The Wilderness Trail.
Hill, Leonard, John Johnston and the Indians.
Hutchins, Thomas, Papers of Sir John Johnston.
Indiana Historical Society Publications.

James, J. Alton, The Life of George Rogers Clark.
Kellogg, Louise P., The Old Northwest.
Lossing, Benson, The Pictorial Field Book of the War of 1812.
McAfee, Robert B., History of War of 1812.
McAvoy, Thomas T., The Catholic Church in Indiana.
McCoy, Isaac, History of the Baptist Indian Missions.
McGinness, John, Biography of Frances Slocum.
Mohr, Walter H., Federal Indian Relations.
O'Meara, Walter, Guns at the Forks.
Parkman, Francis, Count Frontenac and New France under Louis XIV.
Peake, Ora B., History of the Indian Factory System.
Peckham, Howard H., Pontiac and the Indian Uprising.
Porter, Kenneth W., John Jacob Astor.
Quaife, Milo M., Journal of Henry Hay.
Riley, Captain James, Early Travels to Fort Wayne.
Roosevelt, Theodore, The Winning of the West.
Roberts, Bessie K., The Frontier Post.
Royce, Charles, Indian Land Concessions in the United States.
Schoolcraft, Henry R., History of Indian Tribes.
Slocum, Charles E., History of Maumee River Basin.
Smith, Dwight L., Wayne's Peace with the Indians of the Old Northwest.
Smith, William H., Bouquet's Expedition Against the Indians.
St. Clair, General Arthur, Papers edited by W. H. Smith.
Teas, Thomas, Trip to Three Rivers.
Thwaites, Reuben G., Early Western Travels.
Wayne, Anthony, Correspondence on the Northwest Campaign.
Volney, Constantin F. S., Aboriginal Tribes of America.
Wilkinson, General James, Memoirs of My Own Times.
Winger, Otho, The Frances Slocum Trail.
War Department, Official Communications.
Young, Calvin M., Little Turtle the Great Chief of the Miamis.
Fort Wayne Journal.
Fort Wayne Sentinel.
U. S. Territorial Papers, Volumes on Northwest and Indiana.